D1597740

THE AMERICAN
DIESEL LOCOMOTIVE

Frisco's Capleville yard near Memphis, Tennessee.
(Courtesy of Saint Louis-San Francisco Railway.)

THE AMERICAN DIESEL LOCOMOTIVE

Arthur J. Roberts

SOUTH BRUNSWICK AND NEW YORK: A.S. BARNES AND COMPANY
LONDON: THOMAS YOSELOFF LTD

A.S. Barnes and Co., Inc.
Cranbury, New Jersey 08512

Thomas Yoseloff Ltd
Magdalen House
136-148 Tooley Street
London SE1 2TT, England

Library of Congress Cataloging in Publication Data

Roberts, Arthur J
    The American Diesel locomotive.

    Bibliography: p.
    Includes index.
       1. Diesel locomotives—United States—History.
I.   Title.
TJ619.R6   385'.36'60973   74-30722
ISBN 0-498-01667-6

This is a presentation in name and interest of those who wish they knew something about our country's railroads, and in particular, about the locomotives that propel their trains. Knowing about things makes them less awesome, less boring, and overwhelming. Everyone has problems, even railroads. They need a little love, too.

PRINTED IN THE UNITED STATES OF AMERICA

CONTENTS

5

ACKNOWLEDGMENTS

Special acknowledgment goes to the late Mrs. Roy B. McKee for her continuing inspiration.

Further acknowledgment goes to: Donald Alsted; L.G. Anders; James Bush; William Copeland; U. William Cunitz; John B., Egan; John E. Green; L.C. Green; S.S. Lingenfelter; R.P. McFeeters; John Michael; Anne K. Pratt; Margaret B. Roberts; Janet Robinson; Ed Robinson; Sarah R. Strouss; Larry Ryan; Charity Roberts; C. Arthur Roberts; Thomas Stewart; W.A. Bliss, Jr.; Gordon P. Barth; A. Bagnoli; Russell Vacanti; Lupe Robles — B&O (Chessie System); the late C.A. Kennedy — B&O (Chessie System); Stephen Ailes and Joe W. Grotegut — Association of American Railroads; Bill Gehrt, John Tilson, and Bill Burk — Atchison, Topeka, and Santa Fe Railway Company; Richard W. Sprague — Bangor and Aroostook Railroad Company; R.R. Firestone — Bessemer and Lake Erie Railroad Company; Albert M. Rung and P.W. Stafford — Burlington Northern Railroad Company; David Jones — Canadian Pacific; C. Romani, W.H. Cyr, and Susan Gallagher — Canadian National Railways; C.C. Dilley — Chicago, Milwaukee, Saint Paul, and Pacific Railroad Company; Edward J. Wojtas — Chicago, Rock Island, and Pacific Railroad Company; Thomas J. Judge — Chicago, Northwestern Transportation Company; John W. Terrill — Colorado and Southern Railway Company; George W. Hockaday — Delaware and Hudson Railway Company; A. Rosenberger — Denver and Rio Grande Western Railroad Company; F.S. Moorehead — Detroit, Toledo, and Ironton Railroad Company; A.C. Hanson — Duluth, Missabe and Iron Range Railway Company; Robert J. Schiek — Elgin, Joliet, and Eastern Railway Company; Martin M. Pomphrey — Saint Louis-San Francisco Railway Company; Clifford G. Massoth — Illinois Central Gulf Railroad; R.J. Blair — Kansas City Southern Railway Company; W. Gifford Moore — Lehigh and Hudson River Railway Company; L.M. Noseworthy — Lehigh Valley Railroad Company; Edison H. Thomas — Louisville and Nashville Railroad Company (The Family Lines System); Bradley L. Peters — Maine Central Railroad Company; Harry E. Hammer — Missouri Pacific Lines; D.A. Flammia, Jr. — Norfolk Southern Railway Company (Southern Railway System); Peyton B. Winfree, Jr. — Norfolk and Western; J.V. Mack — Reading Company; J.J. Newbauer, Jr. — Richmond, Fredericksburg, and Potomac Railroad Company; Donald T. Martin — (SCL/L&N) Seaboard Coast Line/Louisville & Nashville, (The Family Lines System); John C. Bergene — Soo Line Railroad Company; A.S. Eggerton, Jr. — Southern Railway System; Timothy L. Johnson— Southern Pacific Transportation Company; J.A. Hill and I.L. Dorsey — Toronto, Hamilton, and Buffalo Railway Company; Barry B. Combs — Union Pacific Railroad Company; G.M. Leilich — Western Maryland Railway Company; Paul Gordenev — Western Pacific Railroad; R.R. Powers — General Electric Company; Richard P. Vogt — General Motors Corporation.

INTRODUCTION

The diesel locomotive has supplanted the steam locomotive in the United States and most of the rest of the world and has been resented for it ever since. Railfans moan, railroaders (except ex-firemen) heave a heavy sigh of reserved consternation, and the public turns the other cheek, hardly pausing to notice the absence of soft-coal soot on their laundry. But whatever is resisted persists and persist the diesel has.

At large in this country and Canada today are a collection of new generations that are not very much in touch with things their predecessors knew well. Today's younger people, and even a large portion of the premiddle-agers, have, at best, a very vague notion of what really constitutes a railroad, and why those pieces of equipment owned by a railroad are important to it. Most of the children now have a television to watch while they play with their model-automobile race sets, at the same time in age that their fathers played with model trains in the attic.

Allegedly the romance of railroading disappeared with the lighting of the junk dealers' torch and the melting down of the steam locomotives. Maybe one romance did, but the world did not end that day and railroading has advanced since then, too.

Since the days of steam, some changes have occured to America's railroads. The North American economy has changed over to one of massive transportation by truck, airplane, bus, and the automobile. The railroads, in a sense, have dramatically shrunk from the transportation scene. They are staging a comeback and it has been the diesel that stood between them and extinction.

Since people don't personally use trains as they formerly did, they have got out of touch and familiarity with them. It is almost possible for a person to go through most of his life without being aware of railroads, their cars, or locomotives until that awful day when one of them stops him at a grade crossing and makes him late for an appointment. The late President John F. Kennedy said: "We need not read deeply into the history of the United States to become aware of the great and vital role which the railroads have played in the opening up and development of this great nation."[1]

The following passages from the Association of American Railroads sum up the history and development of America's railroads:

> As our frontier moved westward, it was the railroads that bore the great tide of Americans to areas of new opportunities and new hope. It was the railroads

ALCO FA1 1330 at the Penn Central-New Haven engine terminal in South Boston, 1 May 1969. This entire facility along with repair tracks and coach yards has been eliminated. It is reported that the FA1 went to the Long Island Railroad as a power car for their push-pull commuter trains. (Courtesy of John B. Egan.)

that linked together the diverse segments of this vast land so that together they might create the greatest economy the world has known.

The first locomotive to run on rails in the United States — or in the New World for that matter — was a small experimental engine built by Col. John Stevens and operated on a circular railway track at Hoboken, New Jersey in 1825. It was never put to practical use.

The first locomotive to run on a standard railroad in the United States was the British-built *Stourbridge Lion*. On 8 August 1829, *The Lion*, operated by Horatio Allen, a young civil engineer, was tried out on a short, wooden railroad in Pennsylvania. It proved to be too heavy for the rails.

In September 1829, *The Tom Thumb*, an experimental locomotive built by Peter Cooper of New York, was given a trial run on a newly built railroad in Baltimore, Maryland. This little engine, weighing about one ton, was the first American-built locomotive to run on a common-carrier railroad in this country.

Meanwhile, the pioneer railroad of the South was getting under way at Charleston, South Carolina. In December 1830, scheduled steam-passenger service, the first in America, was introduced on that road.

The first locomotive to pull a train of cars on an American railroad was the *Best Friend* of Charleston, built at the West Point Foundry in New York and shipped to Charleston by sailing vessel. It weighed three-and-a-half tons.

Opening of the first railroads in Maryland and South Carolina in 1839 marked the beginning of the spectacular "railroad era" in America. Forward-looking citizens were quick to recognize the superiority of railroads over other forms of transportation. By 1835, more than 200 railway charters had been granted in eleven states and more than a thousand miles of railroad were in operation. Only a few of the early charter holders actually succeeded in building railroads, and only a few of the early companies survived for any appreciable length of time. However, America had been bitten by the railroad bug. And there was no stopping the new enterprise.

Railroads quickly sprang up in Ohio, Michigan,

Indiana, Illinois, West Virginia, Kentucky, Tennessee, Alabama, Mississippi, and Louisiana, as well as in states bordering the Atlantic. In some instances, the small railroads of the 1830's and 1840's formed the nuclei for — or later became parts of — the important railway systems of today.

By 1850, there were more than 9,000 miles of railroad in the United States. Most of the lines were short. But many of them were connected with other lines to form through-routes for travel and commerce. It was possible, in 1850, to travel all the way from Waterville, Maine to Buffalo, New York by using some twelve different railroads and changing cars several times en route. The trip took about four days.

As late as 1850 there was not a mile of railroad west of the Mississippi River. But the discovery of gold in California, the lure of trans-Pacific trade, and the land-grant policy of the Federal government were giving impetus to westward railway expansion.

The first railroad to be opened west of the Mississippi River was started in Saint Louis, Missouri in 1851. The first locomotive on that pioneer railroad was the *Pacific*, sometimes called *Pacific No. 3*, which arrived at Saint Louis from the East in August 1852, and made its initial run a few miles out of Saint Louis on December 9 of that year.

During the 1850's several railroads were built westward from the Mississippi, and by 1860, the Iron Horse was on the Missouri. Between 1850 and 1860 railway mileage in the United States increased from 9,021 to 30,626 miles. The country was growing by leaps and bounds, largely under the impetus of the railroads. Many railroads were under construction; numerous others were contemplated. One of these was the road across the Great Plains and through the Western mountains to the Pacific Coast — a line two-and-a-half times longer than the longest railroad then existing anywhere else in the world.

In 1863, President Abraham Lincoln fixed the Eastern terminus of the proposed transcontinental railroad at Omaha, Nebraska territory. In California, a company was organized to build a railroad eastward from Sacramento to meet the road from Omaha. Ground was broken at Omaha and Sacramento in 1863, and construction was pushed with vigor. Track laying moved along with amazing speed. Boom towns mushroomed along the right of way as the tracks advanced. Swarms of land-hungry settlers followed in the wake of the rails.

Finally on 10 May 1869, the construction forces met and the rails were joined at Promontory, north of Great Salt Lake. A train from the East and a train from the West approached and halted within a few feet of each other. Then, between the noses of the two locomotives a memorable scene took place. A symbolic golden spike was driven, signalizing the completion of the first chain of railroads to span the American continent.

From Utah to points throughout the nation flashed the thrilling telegraph message: "The last rail is laid. The last spike is driven. The Pacific Railroad is com-

pleted." The golden spike marked the completion of the greatest railway project the world had yet seen. It ended the necessity of long voyages around Cape Horn. It brought an end to the journey by ship to the Isthmus of Panama, the trip through the jungle to the Pacific and then by vessel to California. It also brought an end to the long and perilous overland trip by stagecoach or covered wagon.

The railroad united the East and the West — brought the cities of the Atlantic and the Pacific within a few day's journey of each other and opened up a vast and fertile region for settlement and development.

With the Atlantic and Pacific linked by rail, the conquest of the West was in full swing. During the 1870's and 1880's many other important railway lines were built, opening up large areas of rich territory. In 1881 rails were joined in New Mexico to form the second rail route to the Pacific Coast and the first direct line to South California. In 1883, a railroad was completed between Saint Paul and the Pacific Northwest.

In 1888 a southern route between Chicago and California was completed and in 1893 another great trunk line stretched from the Great Lakes to Puget Sound. Still another route to the Pacific Northwest was completed in 1909, and in 1910 a new rail line was completed from Salt Lake City to San Francisco Bay.

The decade from 1880 to 1890 witnessed the most rapid railway expansion in American history. In that ten-year period, 7,030 miles of railroad a year were added — a total increase of 70,300 miles in a single decade. This unparalleled expansion was not confined to the region west of the Mississippi. Railway mileage in Florida more than quadrupled during the ten-year period. In Mississippi and North Carolina it more than doubled. And in Alabama, Georgia, Kentucky, Michigan, West Virginia, and Wisconsin, it nearly doubled.

The expansion of the railway network continued through the 1890s and, with diminishing pace, up to 1916. By then, every state and nearly every county and important city and town was served by one or more railroads and provided with daily service to and from all parts of the country. As the era of expansion drew to a close, railway lines reached a peak of 254,000 miles in 1916. Since then there has been a steady drop in the aggregate length of road until today it totals 209,000 miles.

As the railroads brought the country closer together physically, it became apparent that the country would have to adopt some sort of uniform time system. There were at least 100 different local times by which trains were operated until 18 November 1883. On that date, the railroads began operating under a new standard time, with the country divided into four time zones that still exist: Eastern, Central, Mountain, and Pacific.

Although this "railroad time" was used by the federal, state, and local governments, it was not until 19 March 1918, that Congress passed the Standard Time

Act, making this the official time.

Time was not the only nonstandardized thing hampering railroad operations. Rail gauges were not standardized either. In 1871, there were no fewer than twenty-three different railway gauges in use in the United States. At various times gauges as wide as six feet and as narrow as two feet were in use. Obviously, efficient long-distance handling of freight and passengers was impossible until track gauges became uniform. By 1887 most American railroads had converted to what has become the standard gauge of four feet, 8½ inches. Almost all rail track in the United States, Canada, and Mexico is a standard gauge. As a result, any shipper in any of these three countries can load a freight car for delivery to any other point.

Early in their history, American railroads realized there were many problems revolving around equipment, schedules, and other matters that could not be solved without cooperation. It was not until 1934, however, that a single organization — the Association of American Railroads (A.A.R.) — was established to coordinate activities and standardize equipment.

But there were many instances of cooperation before then. The A.A.R. itself was formed by a merger of the American Railway Association, the Association of Railway Executives, the Railway Accounting Officers Association, the Bureau of Railway Economics and other organizations. In fact, formal cooperation goes all the way back to the years just after the Civil War when railroads held meetings to find ways of working together on common problems. The A.A.R. can trace its "lineal descent" back to groups like the Master Car Builders Association — formed in 1867 to conduct tests and experiments aimed at standardizing freight cars — and the General Time Convention of Railway Managers.

Headquartered in Washington, D.C., the A.A.R. today represents most of the nation's Class I railroads and conducts many operations for the entire industry. As a result of joint action undertaken through the A.A.R., a standard code of operating rules was adopted, and there are uniform codes to assure that block signals and interlocking devices are operated according to the same rules on most railroads. Other agreements worked out through the A.A.R. involve per diem and demurrage charges so that freight cars can be freely interchanged.

Joint studies and research also have contributed greatly to the development of locomotives and cars, air brakes, automatic couplers, automatic signals, and improved communications. Similarly, engineering standards have been adopted that apply to bridges, rails, ties, and other parts of the railway track structures. Continuing programs of research are carried on by the A.A.R. at its Research Center in Chicago. Staff members work with other departments of the A.A.R., member roads, shippers, and the government in deciding what projects should be undertaken.

The history of railroad passenger service is just

B&O (Baltimore and Ohio—now part of Chessie System) GP40 with Chessie System GP40–2 head for the Ohio River Bridge at Beaver, Pennsylvania. (Photo by author.)

about as old as the history of railroads. The first passenger trains went into operation shortly after the first railroads were completed in the 1830s. Cars on these early trains were crude. They were a lot like stagecoaches. But gradually the equipment was improved. Stove-heated wooden cars, lighted by candles or oil lamps, soon made their appearance. The 1830s also saw the advent of sleeping cars on American railroads, with the first car operating between Harrisburg and Chambersburg, Pennsylvania. Several other railroads operated sleeping cars over the next twenty years, but it was not until George M. Pullman built his first car in 1859 that they came into general use.

Pullman, whose name became synonymous with first-class passenger cars, also played an important role in the introduction of dining service on trains. Although the first dining cars were introduced between Philadelphia and Baltimore in 1863, Pullman's first dining car was built in 1868 and after that they became common on good trains.

Further improvements were made in passenger service over the next few decades. Steam heat and electric lights were introduced before 1900. All-steel passenger cars made their appearance in 1904. And steam locomotives capable of speeds up to 100 miles per hour went into service. By the time World War II began, streamlined passenger trains had been developed. Powered by diesel and electric locomotives, these trains provided the best in speed and comfort. Features included air conditioning, flourescent lighting, safety glass, all private-room sleeping cars, and, on some trains after the war, dome cars.

As soon as the war ended, American railroads poured hundreds of millions of dollars into new passenger equipment, and it was generally regarded as the best the world had ever seen. At first the public flocked to the new trains. But even as they were being introduced, traveling habits were changing. Fueled by the lifting of wartime restrictions, and by billions of dollars in public funds that improved highways and airports, the private car and the commercial plane began attracting most of the travelers who formerly went by train. The long-haul passenger train could not compete with the convenience of the automobile or the speed of the plane. The result was a substantial reduction in the number of such trains as railroads sought to reduce growing passenger losses.

But, if recent years have brought less need for long-haul passenger trains, they have also seen an increased need for commuter trains. New equipment like double-deck and self-propelled cars is being used to speed the suburban dweller to and from his job in the city. Between 1962 and 1968 commutation traffic increased from slightly more than four billion miles to almost 4.4 billion. This number will inevitably grow.[2]

A diesel-electric locomotive is a self-contained, diesel engine-powered, electric-motor driven power plant on wheels that moves freight and/or passengers from one point along its own roadbed to another point or destination. According to Webster, a locomotive is "an engine that can move about by its own power; especially an electric, steam, or diesel engine on wheels designed to push or pull a railroad train."[3]

Diesel locomotives are really a combination of diesel-power and electric-power systems. A diesel engine, running on fuel oil — a distillate of petroleum — drives a direct-current generator. The generator makes electricity, that drives the traction motors located on the axles of the locomotives. The traction motors turn the axles that turn the wheels causing the locomotive to move. The diesel engine is known as the *prime mover*.

The diesel engine also drives an alternating-current generator called *an alternator*. Alternating current is used to run the traction motor blowers that cool the traction motors. Alternating current also powers the cooling fans that cool the engine water and oil.

If a diesel locomotive is equipped with dynamic brakes, direct current is supplied to fans that dissipate heat from the braking operation. Dynamic braking is an operation of using the locomotive's traction motors as drag brakes by reversing the current to them making them act like generators. In the process, the traction motors, now being made to function as generators, create a tremendous amount of energy that is conducted to grids on the locomotive side or roof and is dissipated as heat (very much like a huge space heater).

An auxillary generator, driven from the diesel engine, produces current for the storage batteries, lighting system, control functions, fuel-pump op-

eration, and to power the steam generator if the locomotive has one.

For passenger service, a diesel locomotive has to have a steam generator to provide heat to the cars. The steam generator has several sets of coiled water tubing, totaling several hundred feet in length. Feed water, after passing through the heat exchanger and then a series of coils, goes into the steam generator. As the water progresses through the coils, it is converted to steam. Heat is furnished by the combustion of diesel-fuel oil, which is sprayed by compressed air through a fuel-atomizing nozzle into a firepot above the coils. Hot gases, now exhaust, flow down, then up, and through the coils out to the exhaust stack.

There is an air compressor, driven from the engine via a flexible coupling, that supplies air pressure for the train and locomotive air brakes.

One of the monumental achievements of diesel-locomotive design, that was also the most critical for its operation, was the development of the electric transmission. The diesel locomotive must be able to handle a fixed horsepower with a widely varying demand of voltage and current. This called for specially designed field windings in the generator and also a load-control device, that works on the specially designed control field to insure a constant horsepower demand on the engine.

According to *Railroads of America*, a publication of the A.A.R.:

> The first diesel locomotive placed in service in the United States was a switcher on the Central Railroad of New Jersey in 1925. The Chicago Burlington and Quincy (now Burlington Northern) and the Union Pacific railroads were the first to use the diesel on passenger trains. Both roads began using them on mainline service in 1934. The Santa Fe placed the first diesels in regular service in 1940. By the mid-1950s most U.S. railroads had shifted the bulk of their locomotive power from steam to diesels. Steam was not completely phased out on Class I railroads until the early 1960s.

Today diesel locomotives have been developed that can generate as much as 6,600 horsepower in a single unit.[4]

This in itself is a remarkable feat when one considers that in the not too distant past the diesel engine by itself was not at all suitable for delivering much power.

The diesel engine was developed by a German named Rudolph Diesel. Dr. Diesel operated his first successful engine in 1897. It delivered twenty-five horsepower. But the first diesel engines were so heavy in proportion to the horsepower they developed that they seemed of dubious use to the railroad industry. But through research largely by the Electro-Motive Division of General Motors and by General Electric, diesel engines were finally built that were not terribly heavy to gain higher horsepower.

In the United States today there are about 560 operating railroads. Of these, seventy-four are Class I line-haul roads and 486 are switching and terminal companies or Class II railroads. Line-haul railroads are those that provide service between terminal points in the flow of commerce. In all, in the United States, there are nearly 27,000 locomotives in use, the vast majority of them diesel-electric. In Canada there are almost 4,000 diesels, and nineteen electrics at work. Mexico has approximately 766 diesels, thirty-five steamers, and nine electrics.[5]

Despite any appearance to the contrary, there are many differences in diesel locomotives. There are over 135 individual models of diesel locomotives in use in North America and, though they perform a common function of moving passengers and freight and have a common method of construction and operation, that is essentially the limit of their likeness.

Diesel locomotives are divided into groups called *classes*, according to their designed function and horsepower available to work. The first of these classes is the *road locomotives*, those used in major freight hauling over long distances. They include the streamlined, carbody style known as *covered wagons*, as well as the long-bodied, heavy giants like the ALCO 636 and larger. They pull heavy freight for long distances at high speeds. Seldom are they used alone, but more often than not with other road locomotives of similar or roughly similar horsepower and weight. When several of them are connected together to pull one train, they are controlled by the engineer in the leading unit by means of what is known as *multiple-unit control*. Multiple-unit control is an electrical linkage between the locomotives that permits the operation of all the connected locomotives from one cab, as if the group was one huge locomotive.

Within the class of road locomotives, there are many individual models. One of the determining factors in choosing the number and horsepower capability of locomotives to pull their freight is the consideration of maintaining a schedule. There are a great variety of combinations of road locomotives that could pull any given train, but to maintain speed and time, the locomotives vary with the size and weight of the train.

The next class of locomotives represented in North America are the *road switchers* or *general-purpose locomotives*. They are used for short-haul freight work, are lighter trains, and also are used in conjunction with road locomotives when needed and if they have multiple-unit control capability. As a class they are shorter, lighter, and generally of lesser horsepower than the road locomotives. They can do large-scale switching and, as the name *general purpose*, implies, a varied assortment of tasks. The trend in locomotive manufacturing has been toward more of this class of locomotive, one which adapts itself to many situations, thereby not restricting it to only limited use. Limited use only means to a railroad that it has an expensive piece of equipment in the sense that it is not adaptable.

Then there are, and in many instances, were, the *passenger locomotives*. These locomotives that can properly be termed *passenger locomotives* that are still in use today are in a great minority. Many are old, having been built in the 1940s and early 1950s. When built, they were the most powerful diesel locomotives in service. They had to be, for passenger trains were long and heavy. There was also the need to keep the train on a relatively tight schedule, which meant that these locomotives had to develop a lot of speed.

Passenger locomotives are long bodied, streamlined in appearance, and aging. They are also declining in number because their performance at passenger-train hauling is very poorly attended by the public. Now with Amtrak in operation, there is a rebirth in passenger travel.

There is one class of locomotive that is a crossbreed between the freight locomotives and the passenger models. That is the *freight-passenger diesel*. The older models were longer than their freight counterparts, but shorter than the passenger models. Their horsepower rating was the same as that of the freight, which in the older models was lower than the passenger diesels. There are freight-passenger units being built now that are very large and powerful. As a class, these locomotives are equipped with steam generators for heating their trains. This is a prerequisite for any locomotive to pull a passenger train.

The last major class of diesel locomotives are the quiet workhorses of any railroad. They are the *switchers*. These are small-bodied, short locomotives that are geared to move heavy loads from the yards and mainlines of America into the small towns, plants, and industries. It was in the operation of switching that the diesel locomotive made its debut and it is here that it has proliferated, being in numbers nearly the largest class of locomotives. Their outward appearance has remained largely unchanged over the many years of their existence, model to model. They are still short, still plain looking, and still working in the out-of-the-way places.

But there have been changes inside the short bodies that are worthy of note. "Today's freight cars are bigger than ever before, with an average capactiy of 64.9 tons, up nineteen tons in the last forty years."[6] This has caused the breeding of a new generation of switchers as well as all other locomotives. The newest switchers now have as much horsepower as their road-locomotive cousins did ten to fifteen years ago. And as the trend for bigness and heaviness carries on, they will likely get more powerful still.

There is a group of locomotives that could properly be called a *subclass*. These are the *slave* units or *boosters*. They are unmanned units interspersed in long, heavy freight trains for operation in mountainous country. Such helper units are equipped with automatic control systems, including tiny, coupling-strain gauges that read power requirements and permit automatic throttle adjustments.[7]

There are also boosters that are not nearly as sophisticated in their control as the automatically controlled ones. These are known as *B-units*, and, through multiple-unit control, are used directly behind or in amongst power units that have control panels. B-units are not uncommon, but still are in a minority as far as locomotives are concerned. They are the ones with no cabs that otherwise look like locomotives. The fact that they do not have control cabs is their chief disadvantage. They can only be used to help other locomotives, but can not pull a train by themselves. This puts them in the class of the vanishing specialist, the opposite of the truly independent locomotive.

It is not too unusual to find that there are more of some models of locomotives in use currently than others. There were over 3,800 EMD GP-9s built between 1954 and 1960. Many of them are still working today. This is one of the largest numbers of an individual model of locomotive produced. The ALCO RSD7, produced in 1954, was a short production of two units. It was a 2,250 horsepower road switcher.

Not nearly all the diesels produced, nor all the models built, are in existence today. Some of the diesel-locomotive manufacturers themselves have closed down their operations. The American Locomotive Company, once a great builder of steam locomotives and later a substantial builder of some very famous diesels, is no longer in operation. From their Schenectady, New York shops rolled many a powerful steam locomotive. After World War II, they built the famous FA series of freight locomotives that were in the competitive class of the Electro-Motive Division's F3s, F7s, and F9s, They built that much revered PA series of passenger locomotives.

Now most of the FA and PA streamlined locomotives of ALCO are gone. The company still lives on through its tremendous number of switching locomotives and its later model road locomotives and road switchers. ALCO products are being built under the guiding hand of the Montreal Locomotive Works that bought out ALCO. The Montreal Locomotive Works is a very prolific builder of locomotives for Canadian railroads.

The Baldwin Locomotive Works, at one time the foremost manufacturer of steam locomotives, was slow to expand into the diesel market and is not now manufacturing diesel locomotives. Baldwin built a competitive line of locomotives that were famous in their own right. Their DR-4-4-15 freight locomotive was comparable to the ALCO FA1 or the EMD F7. It was built in both A-and B-units. The Baldwin RF16 compared to the ALCO FA2 and was of higher horsepower than the EMD F7 at 1,600. There was also an RF16 B-unit. Baldwin built a line of numerous diesel switchers, too. They manufactured the big six-axle, 1,600-horsepower, AS616 (still in service on the Union Pacific), the S6, S7, S10, RS10, RS12, and S12. Even today the Baldwin Locomotive Works makes replacement parts for their locomotives, though locomotive production itself is a thing of the past.

Fairbanks-Morse was another locomotive builder who entered the market with diesels too late in the game to really pull off major success. Fairbanks-Morse, like Baldwin, was strong in the switcher line. Though some of their products are still operating, the bulk of them has gone to the happy locomotive hunting ground. They built the high-bodied, slim H-10-44, H-12-44, H-16-44, H-12-66, H-16-66, and H-24-66, to name a few. And they are not all faded away, either. The Canadian National and the Milwaukee Road still operate the H-16-44s. The Milwaukee still has H-16-66s and the Santa Fe runs its H-12-44s, as does the Burlington Northern. The Canadian National has the H-24-66 in service.

But the Fairbanks CFA-16-4, 1,600- horsepower, streamlined freight locomotive, is a thing of the past. It, along with its B units, is gone. Also gone are its 1,750-horsepower cousins, the passenger locomotives.

The locomotive manufacturers of today are the Electro-Motive Division of General Motors, the General Electric Company, and the Montreal Locomotive Works. These are the major builders who have survived to this day. Theirs is the equipment that is most in evidence, though many ALCO

A Baldwin S12 parked off to one side in Altoona, Pennsylvania. The remnants of another locomotive can be seen in the foreground. This was the end for 8130, but several of these locomotives are in use at U.S. Steel in Youngstown, Ohio, and elsewhere. (Photo by author.)

ALCO HH660 yard switchers being scrapped at the Southhampton Street yard in South Boston, Massachusetts in June 1969. (Courtesy of John B. Egan.)

Baldwin RS12 on its way to the final resting place in the scrap yard. It is seen here standing in a freight train in Conway yard, north of Pittsburgh, Pennsylvania. Forty-six of these were built between 1951–55. (Photo by author.)

An S1, built by ALCO, being switched itself for its last ride to the discard pile. This locomotive and the RS12 above were spliced into the same freight train en route to scrapping. 724 S1s were built from 1940–50. (Photo by author.)

death. As they grow old and need more and more maintenance, the owner railroads will be very hard pressed to keep them in service. Eventually, as newer models by competitors arrive on the market, the older models will be sold off or scrapped. Small terminal railroads and industrial plants may be able to use these discards for years. Larger railroads would not be able to afford to keep them.

Another facet of railroading that works against some locomotives is their lack of capacity to work in conjunction with other locomotives the individual railroads own. Since many freight and large switching operations require several locomotives working together, all the grouped locomotives must have compatible electrical systems and control capabilities. Initially in the construction of diesel locomotives, there was not a set of standards that all manufacturers followed regarding similar controlling devices. This meant that right from the start some locomotives could only work with their own kind and could not be of universal service to the railroads.

Nowadays, nearly all locomotives have multiple-unit control and will pull trains with different locomotives. But before this was true, it sentenced a locomotive to the category of a special case. Special cases are very expensive to a railroad. It means that they own locomotives that can only be used some of the time rather than in any given situation. Diesel locomotives were a major advance in standardization themselves that eliminated the huge diversity of steam locomotives. But until there was true universal function among diesel locomotives, the oddball would be in a tenuous survival position.

units remain and very much smaller proportions of Baldwin and Fairbanks can be found.

There were several factors that played a part in the demise of locomotive lines. Probably the worst thing that could happen to a locomotive is the cessation of operations by its builder. This sounds the death knell for such a stranded locomotive or locomotives, since the builder will no longer be supplying the railroads that own their locomotives with replacement parts, engineering advances, and new models. In itself, the closing of the builders' doors dooms the locomotives to a slow, certain

Multiple-units, three F7As, one F7B, and two GP38s, operating in Freedom, Pennsylvania, on the Penn Central. (Photo by author.)

Canadian National oil-burning steam locomotive, No. 6218, photographed in the Fort Erie yards in the winter of 1973. It has been put on display in Fort Erie, Ontario—a gift by the railroad to the public. (Photo by author.)

1
SWITCHING LOCOMOTIVES

Grouped by manufacturer in the approximate
order of their appearance on American railroads.

S1

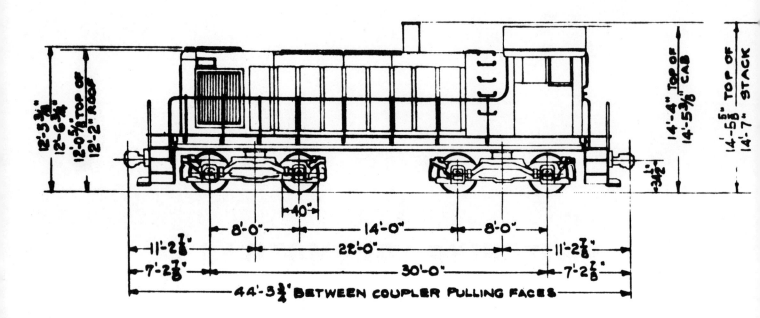

Horsepower	600
Engine	1 – 6 cylinder
	ALCO Model 539
Main Generator	1 GE Model 552 A1 or A3
Traction Motors	4 GE Model 731 A1 or C1
Wheels	40″
Air Brakes	14EL
Wheel Base	
each truck	8′–0″
truck centers	22′–0″
locomotive	30′–0″
Maximum Dimensions	
height	14′–7″
between coupler pulling faces	44′ – 5–3/4″
Fuel capacity	635 gal.
Speed	45 mph.
Builder	ALCO (American
	Locomotive Company)

(Courtesy of G. P. Barth.)

S1

Montpelier and Barre No. 29, an ex-Boston and Maine S1, caught at Montpelier, Vermont, and about to leave with a fan trip to Barre, Vermont, and on up the mountain to the Rock of Ages Granite Quarry. The grade to the quarry requires a series of switchbacks to gain the altitude. (Courtesy of John B. Egan.)

New York Central No. 836, an S1, is shown at the site of the old Boston and Albany engine terminal, since rebuilt due to construction of the Massachusetts turnpike. This was May 1965. No. 836 is Penn Central No. 9320. (Courtesy of John B. Egan.)

S1

S1 switcher, No. 665, belongs to the Youngstown
Sheet and Tube Company in Youngstown, Ohio.
Here it is, without a job, on a warm Saturday after-
noon. (Photo by author.)

Portland Terminal Company, No. 1005, S1, in Grand
Trunk yards in Portland, Maine, after making an
interchange delivery from the Maine Central. The
Portland Terminal is a terminal or short-line railroad. (Courtesy of John B. Egan.)

S2

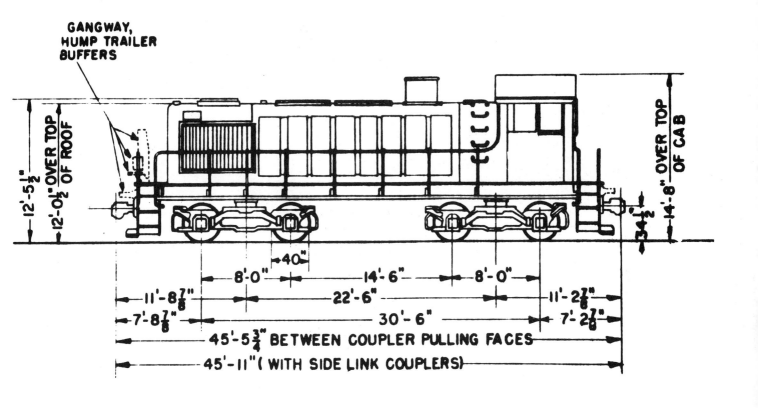

GANGWAY, HUMP TRAILER BUFFERS

12'-5½" OVER TOP OF ROOF

12'-0½" OVER TOP OF ROOF

14'-8" OVER TOP OF CAB

3'-4½"

40"

8'-0"   14'-6"   8'-0"

11'-8⅞"   22'-6"   11'-2⅞"

7'-8⅞"   30'-6"   7'-2⅞"

45'-5¾" BETWEEN COUPLER PULLING FACES

45'-11" (WITH SIDE LINK COUPLERS)

Horsepower	1,000
Engine	1 – 6 cylinder
	ALCO Model 539
Main Generator	1 GE Model 553–C3
Traction Motors	4 GE Model 731–D3 or D2
Wheels	40″
Air Brakes	14EL
Wheel Base	
each truck	8′–0″
truck centers	22′–6″
locomotive	30′–6″
Maximum Dimensions	
height	14′–8″
between coupler pulling faces	45′ – 5–3/4″
Fuel capacity	635 gal.
Speed	45 mph.
Builder	ALCO

(Courtesy of G. P. Barth.)

S2

Penn Central S2, No. 9707, quietly idling away on a summer afternoon in Tonawanda yards, Tonawanda, New York. (Photo by author.)

Canadian Pacific (now known as CP Rail) No. 7096, an American built S2, at Saint Johnsbury, Vermont. Barely visible in the background is Maine Central F7 A-unit, No. 681. (Courtesy of John B. Egan.)

No. 50, S2, of the Buffalo Creek at the Buffalo Creek roundhouse. The Buffalo Creek is a flour-hauling railroad serving the flour mills in Buffalo, New York. (Photo by author.)

S3

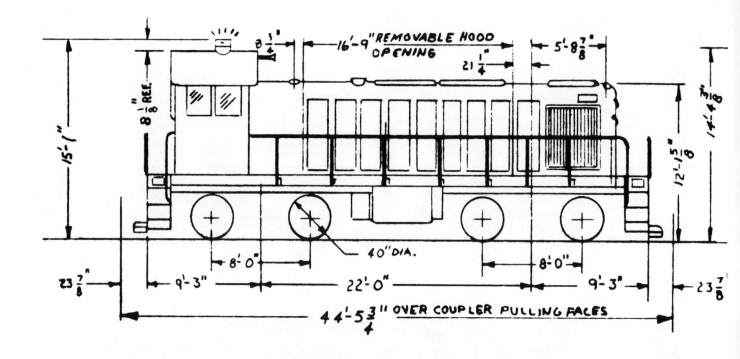

Horsepower	660
Engine	1 – 6 cylinder
Main Generator	1 GE Model GT 552A
Traction Motors	4 GE Model 731
Wheels	40″
Air Brakes	14EL
Wheel Base	
each truck	8′
truck centers	22′
Maximum Dimensions	
height	15′–1″
between coupler pulling faces	44′–5–3/4″
Fuel capacity	635 gals.
Speed	60 mph.
Builder	ALCO

(Courtesy of Ann Arbor Railroad.)

S3

No. 6514, S3 of the Canadian Pacific Rail in front of an SD40, No. 5504, in the Toronto yards. S3s have A.A.R.-type A trucks while S1s have Blunt trucks. S1s and S3s are in most other respects similar. (Photo by author.)

In the early 1960s, the Boston and Maine kept a unit at Berlin, New Hampshire, for their own emergency use. The Berlin Mills Railway made use of each one to supplement their own two-unit roster. S3, No. 1181, shown on the Berlin Mills Railway with engineman Pat Jeffery and fireman T.E. Gillespie. (Courtesy of John B. Egan.)

S4

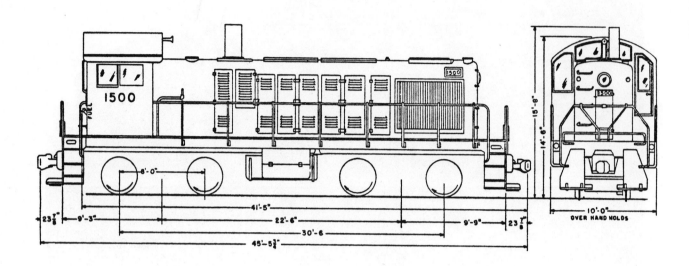

Horsepower	1,000
Engine	1 – 6 cylinder
	Model 539
Main Generator	1 GE Model GT–553
Traction Motors	4 GE Model GE–731
Wheels	40″
Air Brakes	14EL
Wheel Base	
each truck	8′
truck centers	22′–6″
Maximum Dimensions	
height	14′–6″
between coupler pulling faces	45′–11–3/4″
Fuel capacity	635 gals.
Speed	60 mph.
Builder	ALCO

(Courtesy of Atchison, Topeka, and Santa Fe Railroad.)

No. 222 Youngstown and Northern, a subsidiary of the Bessemer and Lake Erie Railroad, S4 pulling a string of gondola cars out of the U.S. Steel plant in Youngstown, Ohio. S4s differ from S2s in that the S4s ride on A.A.R.-type A trucks instead of Blunt trucks. The same is true of S1s and S3s. (Photo by author.)

Canadian National S4, No. 8142, sits out the winter in the Canadian National yards past the Spadina Street Bridge in Toronto, Ontario. (Photo by author.)

S4

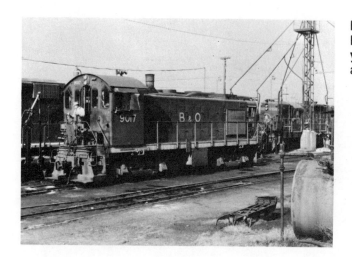

Baltimore and Ohio (part of the Chessie System) S4, No. 9017, waiting for fueling in Baltimore and Ohio yards in New Castle, Pennsylvania. (Photo by author.)

Western Maryland No. 146, S4, switcher. (Courtesy of Western Maryland Railroad.)

S8

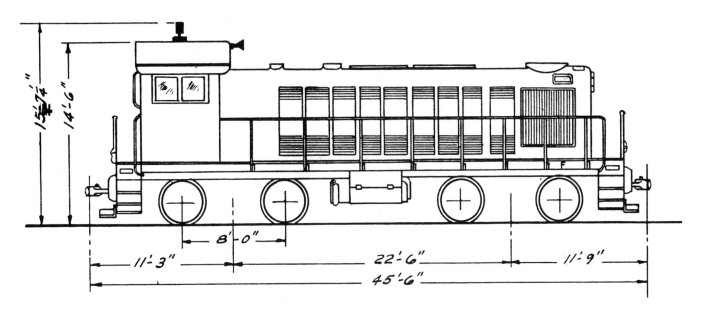

Horsepower	1,000
Engine	1 – 6 cylinder
Main Generator	1 GE Model GT 553
Traction Motors	4 GE Model 731 C2
Wheels	40″
Air Brakes	14EL
Wheel Base	
each truck	8′
truck centers	22′–6″
Maximum Dimensions	
height	15′–7–1/4″
between coupler pulling faces	45′–6″
Fuel Capacity	635 gals.
Speed	60 mph.
Builder	ALCO

(Courtesy of Louisville and Nashville Railroad.)

Canadian Pacific (CP Rail) No. 6617, Montreal Locomotive Works S11 switcher in the CP Rail yards in Toronto. This model entered the Canadian marketplace in 1958. (Photo by author.)

SW1

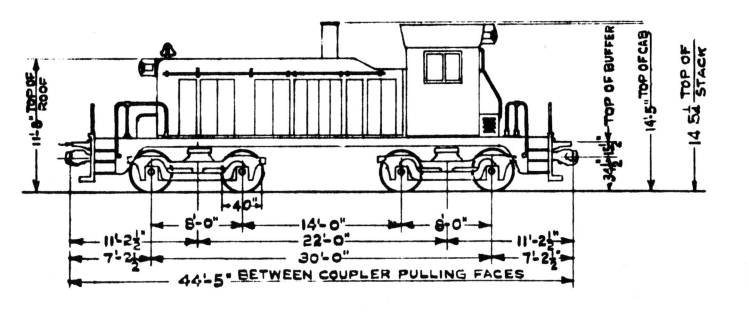

Horsepower	600
Engine	1 – 6 cylinder
	EMD Model 567
Main Generator	1 EMD Model D15C
Traction Motors	4 EMD Model D27
Wheels	40″
Air Brakes	14EL
Wheel base	
each truck	8′–0″
truck centers	22′–0″
locomotive	30′–0″
Maximum dimensions	
Width	10′–0″
height	14′–4–5/8″
between coupler pulling faces	44′–5″
Fuel Capacity	600 gals.
Speed	45 mph.
Builder	EMD (Electro-Motive
	Division of
	General Motors)

(Courtesy of G. P. Barth.)

SW1

Penn Central No. 8597, SW1 in Tonawanda yards, Tonawanda, New York. (Photo by author.)

Boston and Maine SW1, No. 1114, was sold to the Groveton Papers Company and used by them when they furnished their own switching crew. This unit was sold to the Atlanta Stone Mountain Railroad in Georgia after lying idle at Groveton, New Hampshire, for a long period. The Boston and Maine Railroad resumed the switching operations for the paper mill. (Courtesy of John B. Egan.)

NW2

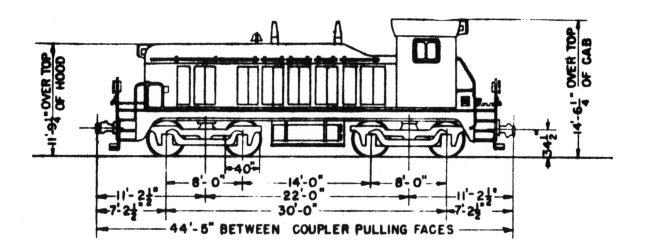

Horsepower	1,000
Engine	1 – 12 cylinder V
Main Generator	1 EMD Model D4D
Traction Motors	4 EMD Model D7, D17, or D27
Wheels	40"
Air Brakes	14EL
Wheel Base	
each truck	8'
truck centers	22'
Maximum Dimensions	
height	14'–6–1/4"
between coupler pulling faces	44'–5"
Fuel capacity	600 gal.
Speed	45 mph.
Builder	EMD

(Courtesy of G. P. Barth.)

Louisville and Nashville No. 2240, NW2, with the masking tape still on it after getting its paint job. (Courtesy of Louisville and Nashville Railroad.)

Toronto, Hamilton, and Buffalo, NW2, No. 54, in Hamilton, Ontario. (Photo by author.)

SW7

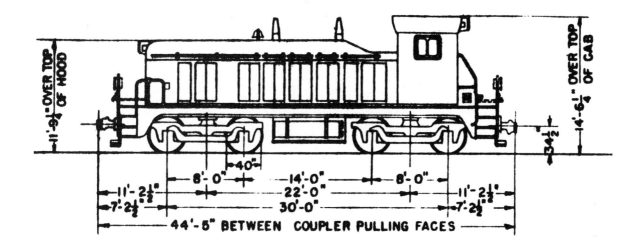

Horsepower	1,200
Engine	1 – 12 cylinder V
Main Generator	1 EMD Model D15A
	or D15C Direct Drive
Traction Motors	4 EMD Model D27
Wheels	40″
Air Brakes	6BL
Wheel Base	
each truck	8′
truck centers	22′
Maximum Dimensions	
height	14′–6–1-/4″
between coupler pulling faces	44′–5″
Fuel capacity	600 gal.
Speed	65 mph.
Builder	EMD

(Courtesy of G. P. Barth)

SW7

Burlington Northern SW7, No. 126. (Courtesy of John E. Green.)

SW8

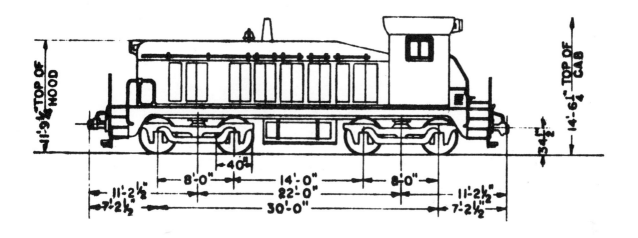

Horsepower	800
Engine	1 – 8 cylinder V
Main Generator	1 – EMD D–15C
Traction Motors	4
Wheels	40″
Air Brakes	6BL
Wheel Base	
each truck	8′
truck centers	22′
Maximum Dimensions	
height	14′–6–1/2″
between coupler pulling faces	44′–5″
Fuel capacity	600 gal.
Speed	65 mph.
Builder	EMD

(Courtesy of G. P. Barth)

SW8

Canadian Pacific No. 6709, an SW8, is an 800 hp. switcher built in the early 1950s. This small locomotive, as with most switchers, seldom leaves the yard areas of a railroad. No. 6709 has a canvas cover over its front radiator to cut down the cold winter air coming into the radiator. (Photo by author.)

SW9

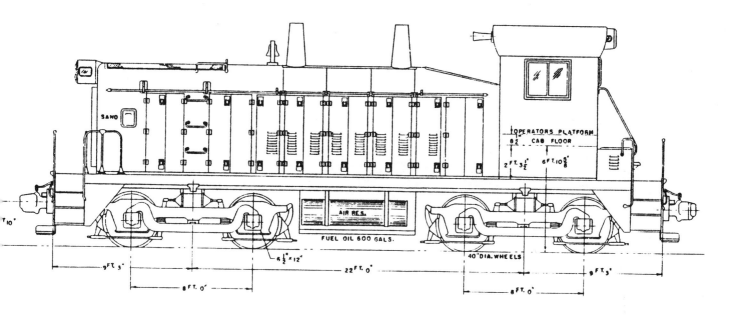

Horsepower	1,200
Engine	1 – 12 cylinder
Main Generator	1 Model D15C
Traction Motors	4 Model D27
Wheels	40″
Air Brakes	6BL
Wheel Base	
each truck	8′
truck centers	22′
Maximum Dimensions	
height	14′–6–1/4″
between coupler pulling faces	44′–5″
Fuel capacity	600 gal.
Speed	65 mph.
Builder	EMD

(Courtesy of
Electro-Motive Division of General Motors Corporation.)

SW9

The Pittsburgh, Chartiers, and Youghiogheny Railroad, which is a short-terminal railroad, owns No. 3, an SW9, a 1,200 hp. switcher built by the Electro-Motive Division of General Motors. (Photo by author.)

SW900

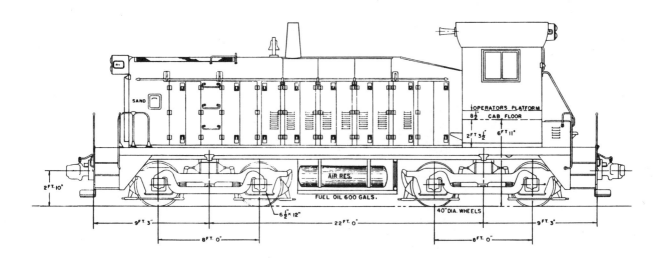

Horsepower	900
Engine	1 – 8 cylinder V
	GM Model 567
Main Generator	1 EMD Model D15C
Traction Motors	4 EMD Model D–37
Wheels	40″
Air Brakes	6BL
Wheel Base	
each truck	8′
truck centers	22′
Maximum Dimensions	
height	14′–6–1/2″
between coupler pulling faces	44′–5″
Fuel capacity	600 gals.
Speed	65 mph.
Builder	EMD

(Courtesy of
Electro-Motive Division of General Motors Corporation.)

SW900

Lehigh Valley No. 130, SW900, switcher pulling a train of hoppers and covered hoppers into Bison yard for pickup by the Erie-Lackawanna. The Lehigh Tifft Terminal yard is a few miles south of the Bison yard in Buffalo. (Photo by author.)

SW1000

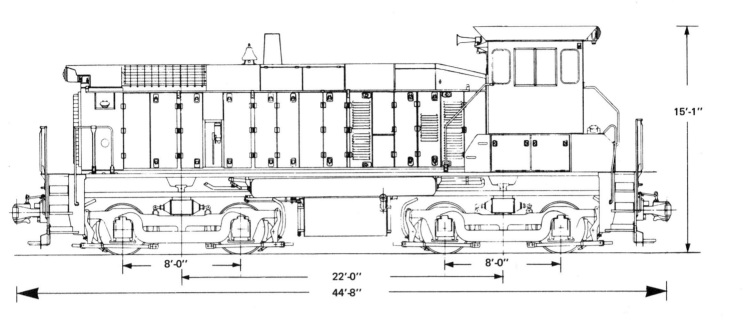

Horsepower	1,000
Engine	1 – 8 cylinder
	EMD Model 8–645E
Main Generator	1 EMD Model D25
Traction Motors	4 EMD Model D77
Wheels	40″
Air Brakes	6BL
Wheel Base	
each truck	8′
truck centers	22′
Maximum Dimensions	
height	15′—1″
between coupler pulling faces	44′–8″
Fuel capacity	1,100 gals.
Builder	EMD

(Courtesy of
Electro-Motive Division of General Motors Corporation.)

SW1200

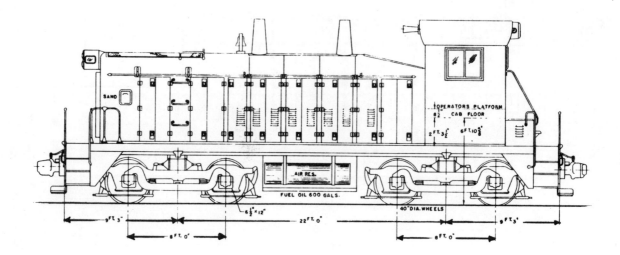

Horsepower	1,200
Engine	1 – 12 cylinder
Main Generator	1 Model D25
Traction Motors	4 Model D67
Wheels	40″
Air Brakes	6BL
Wheel Base	
each truck	8′
truck centers	22′
Maximum Dimensions	
height	14′–6–1/4″
between coupler pulling faces	44′–5″
Fuel capacity	600 gals.
Speed	65 mph.
Builder	EMD

(Courtesy of
Electro-Motive Division of General Motors Corporation.)

SW1200

Erie-Lackawanna No. 454, SW9, idling in the Erie-Lackawanna yards, North Tonawanda, New York. (Photo by author.)

Canadian National No. 7025, SW1200, on the American shore of the Niagara River, after pulling a freight train across the International Bridge from Fort Erie, Ontario, Canada. This is a daily occurrence. (Photo by author.)

SW1500

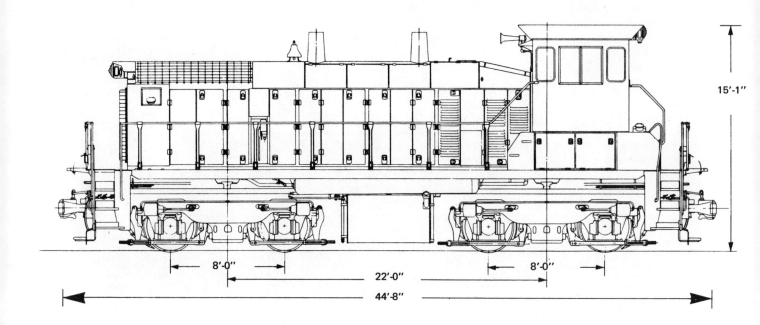

Horsepower	1,500
Engine	1 – 12 cylinder V
	GM Model 12–645E
Main Generator	1 EMD Model D32
Traction Motors	4 EMD Model D–77
Wheels	40″
Air Brakes	6BL
Wheel Base	
each truck	8′
truck centers	22′
Maximum Dimensions	
height	15′—1″
between coupler pulling faces	44′–5″
Fuel capacity	1,100 gals.
Builder	EMD

(Courtesy of
Electro-Motive Division of General Motors Corporation.)

SW1500

Frisco No. 315, SW1500, on turntable at a round-house. The SW1500 is the most powerful switcher on American roads today. (Courtesy of Saint Louis and San Francisco Railroad.)

Penn Central No. 9582, SW1500, pulling cars west-bound past the Penn Central Terminal in Buffalo. (Photo by author.)

2

ROAD-SWITCHING LOCOMOTIVES

Grouped by manufacturer in the approximate
order of their appearance on American railroads.

H–12–44

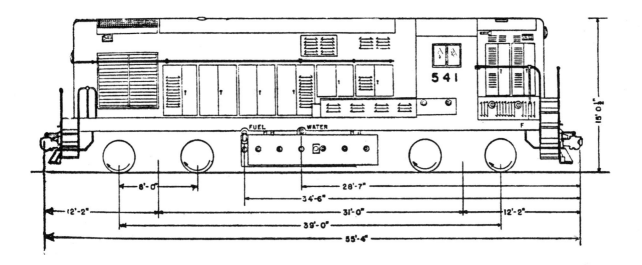

Horsepower	1,200
Engine	1 – 6 cylinder
Main Generator	1 – Westinghouse 481G or 481GZ Direct Driven
Traction Motors	4
Wheels	40″
Air Brakes	6SL
Wheel Base	
each truck	8′
truck centers	25′–6″
Maximum Dimensions	
height	14′–6–5/8″
between coupler pulling faces	49′–2″
Fuel capacity	750 gal.
Speed	60 mph.
Builder	Fairbanks-Morse

(Courtesy of Atchison, Topeka, and Santa Fe Railroad.)

H–16–44

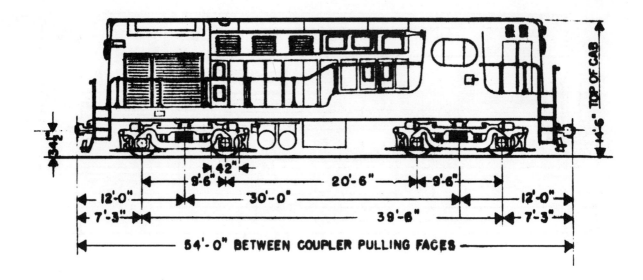

Horsepower	1,600
Engine	1 – 8 cylinder in line
Main Generator	1 – Westinghouse 472A or 472AZ
Traction Motors	4 Westinghouse 370DE or DEZ
Wheels	42″
Air Brakes	6SL
Wheel Base	
each truck	9′–6″
truck centers	30′
Maximum Dimensions	
height	14′–6″
between coupler pulling faces	54′
Fuel capacity	900 gals.
Speed	70 mph.
Builder	Fairbanks-Morse

(Courtesy of G. P. Barth.)

H–16–44

H–16–44, No. 428 of the Milwaukee Road. Built by Fairbanks-Morse. (Courtesy of the Milwaukee Road.)

H–16–66

Six-axle road switcher, Fairbanks-Morse, H–16–66, No. 2127. (Courtesy of the Milwaukee Road.)

Horsepower	1,600
Engine	1 – 8 cylinder
Main Generator	1 Westinghouse 497 B2
Traction Motors	6 Westinghouse 370DE2
Wheels	42″
Air Brakes	6SL
Wheel Base	
each truck	13′
truck centers	37′–6″
Maximum Dimensions	
height	15′
between coupler pulling faces	62′
Fuel capacity	800 gals.
Speed	65 mph.
Builder	Fairbanks-Morse

(Courtesy of the Milwaukee Road.)

H–24–66

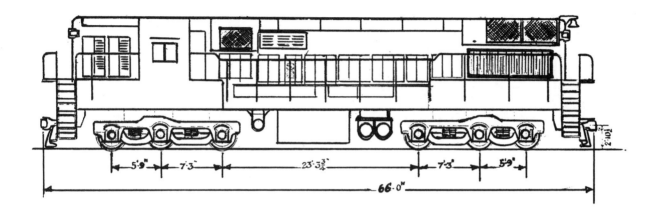

Horsepower	2,400
Engine	1 – 12 cylinder
Main Generator	1 GE Model 5GT 567–C1
Traction Motors	6 GE Model 752 C1
Wheels	40″
Air Brakes	24RL
Wheel Base	
each truck	13′
truck centers	37′–9–3/4″
Maximum Dimensions	
height	15′
between coupler pulling faces	66′
Fuel capacity	1,500 Imperial gals.
Speed	65 mph.
Builder	Fairbanks-Morse

(Courtesy of Canadian National Railways.)

RS1

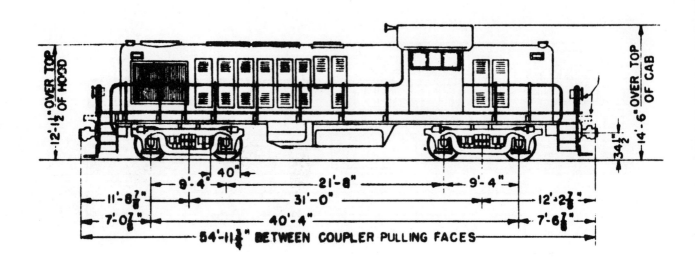

Horsepower	1,000	
Engine	1 – 6 cylinder in line	
	ALCO Model 6–L–25	
Main Generator	1 GE Model GT 553C3 or A	
Traction Motors	4 GE Model 731–D3	
Wheels	40″	
Air Brakes	14EL	
Wheel Base		
each truck	9′–4″	
truck centers	31′–0″	
Maximum Dimensions		
height	14′–6″	
between coupler pulling faces	54′–11–3/4″	
Fuel capacity	1600 gals.	
Speed	60 mph.	
Builder	ALCO	

(Courtesy of G. P. Barth.)

RS1

Penn Central No. 9930, RS1, parked for the weekend in Rochester, New York. The RS1 is a 1,000 hp. road switcher, some of which have been around since World War II. (Photo by author.)

Vermont Railway No. 401, an ex-Rutland Railroad RS1, shown at Rutland, Vermont, yards in May of 1965 shortly after the state of Vermont subsidized the takeover of the northern end of the old Rutland Railroad. (Courtesy of John B. Egan.)

RS2

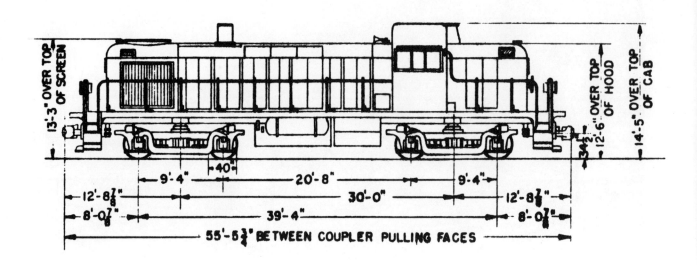

Horsepower	1,500
Engine	1 – 12 cylinder
Main Generator	1 GE Model GT 564
Traction Motors	4 5GE 752A1
Wheels	40″
Air Brakes	6DS
Wheel Base	
each truck	9′–4″
truck centers	30′
Maximum Dimensions	
height	14′–5″
between coupler pulling faces	55'–5–3/4″
Fuel capacity	800 gals.
Speed	65 mph.
Builder	ALCO

(Courtesy of G. P. Barth.)

RS2

Western Maryland, No. 180, RS2, drawn up to the roundhouse. (Courtesy of Western Maryland Railroad.)

Erie-Lackawanna, No. 913, RS2, pushing a train of gondola cars in Youngstown, Ohio. ALCO (American Locomotive Company) built the RS2s. (Photo by author.)

RS3

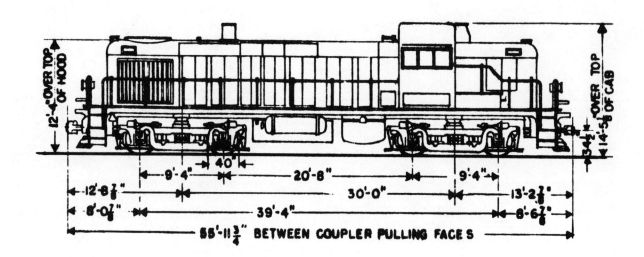

Horsepower	1,600
Engine	1 – 12 cylinder V
	ALCO Model 244
Main Generator	1 GE Model GT 581–A1
Traction Motors	4 GE Model 752–C1 or E1
Wheels	40″
Air Brakes	6–SL
Wheel Bases	
each truck	9′–4″
truck centers	30′
Maximum Dimensions	
height	14′–5–1/8″
between coupler pulling faces	56′–5–3/4″
Fuel capacity	800 gals.
Speed	65 mph.
Builder	ALCO

(Courtesy of G. P. Barth.)

RS3

Louisville and Nashville No. 253, ALCO RS3, 1,600 hp. road switcher. (Courtesy of Louisville and Nashville Railroad.)

Delaware and Hudson, No.4122, RS3 awaiting its orders on a sunny summer day. (Courtesy of George W. Hockaday, Delaware and Hudson Railroad.)

MLW RS10

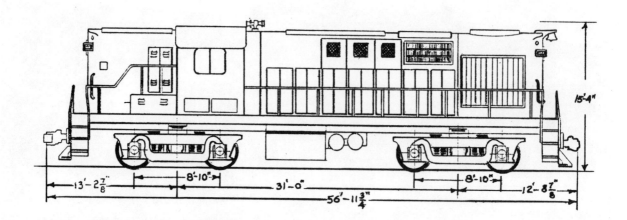

Horsepower	1,600
Engine	1 – 12 cylinder
Main Generator	1 GE Model GT 581
Traction Motors	4 GE Model 752
Wheels	40″
Air Brakes	Westinghouse 24RL
Wheel Base	
each truck	8′–10″
truck centers	31′
Maximum Dimensions	
height	15′–4″
between coupler pulling faces	56′–11–3/4″
Fuel capacity	1,000 Imperial gals.
Speed	75 mph.
Builder	MLW Montreal Locomotive Works

(Courtesy of Canadian National Railways.)

RS11

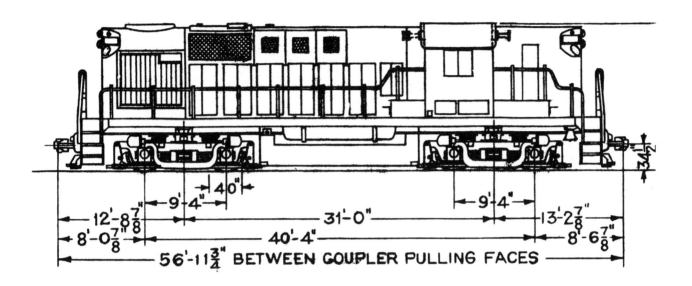

Horsepower	1,800
Engine	1 – 12 Cylinder V
	Model 251
Main Generator	1 GE Model GT 581
Traction Motors	4 GE Model 752
Wheels	40"
Air Brakes	24RL
Wheel Base	
each truck	9'–4"
truck centers	31'
Maximum Dimensions	
height	14'–6"
between coupler pulling faces	56'–11–3/4"
Fuel capacity	1,200 gals.
Speed	92 mph.
Builder	ALCO

(Courtesy of S. S. Lingenfelter.)

RS11

Norfolk and Western No. 2569, ALCO RS11, helping to push cars over the hump at the Bison yards in Buffalo, New York. (Photo by author.)

Delaware and Hudson No. 5005, RS11, shunting cars on a fall day. (Courtesy of George W. Hockaday, Delaware and Hudson Railroad.)

MLW RS18

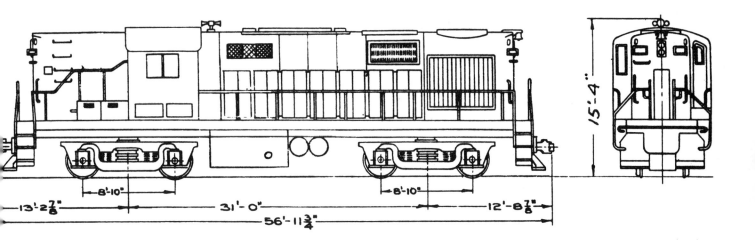

Horsepower	1,800
Engine	1 – 12 cylinder V
Main Generator	1 CGE Model 57–581
Traction Motors	4 CGE Model 752
Wheels	40″
Air Brakes	Westinghouse 26L
Wheel Base	
each truck	8′–10″
truck centers	31′
Maximum Dimensions	
height	15′–4″
between coupler pulling faces	56′–11–3/4″
Fuel capacity	1,000 Imperial gals.
Speed	80 mph.
Builder	MLW

(Courtesy of Canadian National Railways.)

MLW RS18

Canadian Pacific No. 8741, MLW RS18, standing on a siding in the CP Rail yards in Toronto. The MLW RS18 does not bear much resemblance to the ALCO RS18. (Photo by author.)

RS18

Lehigh Valley No. 400, RS18, outside the engine
house at the Tifft Terminal yard in Buffalo. No. 400
weighs 248,200 lbs. and is an 1,800 hp. locomotive.
The Lehigh Valley owns four of these ALCOs.
(Photo by author.)

RS27

Tucked into a corner beside the bridge into Conway yard is No. 2413, an RS27. The Penn Central owns only fifteen of them. They were built by ALCO. (Photo by author.)

RS32

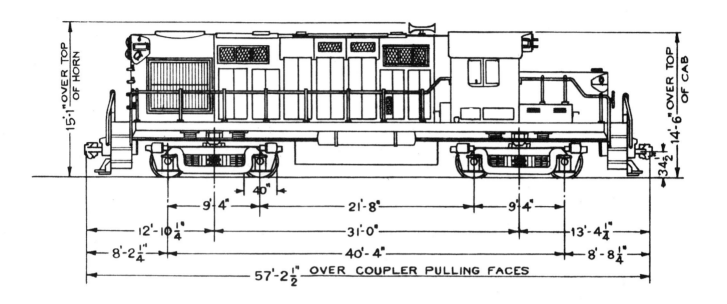

Horsepower	2,000
Engine	1 – 12 cylinder V
Main Generator	1 GE Model 5GT564C1, 566 E1, or 581D1
	Direct Drive
Traction Motors	4 GE Model 752 A1, B1, or C1
Wheels	40″
Air Brakes	26L
Wheel Base	
each truck	9′–4″
truck centers	31′–0″
Maximum Dimensions	
height	15′–1″
between coupler pulling faces	57′–2–1/2″
Fuel capacity	1,200 gals.
Builder	ALCO

(Courtesy of S. S. Lingenfelter.)

RS32

ALCO 2,000 hp., RS32, backing through a switch in Watertown, New York. No. 2040 performs switching operations in Watertown. (Photo by author.)

RS36

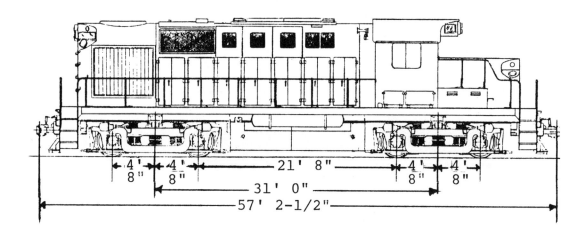

Horsepower	1,800
Engine	1 – 12 cylinder
Main Generator	1 GE Model 5–GT–581
Traction Motors	4 GE Model 752
Wheels	40″
Air Brakes	26L
Wheel Base	
each truck	9′–4″
truck centers	31′
Maximum Dimensions	
height	14′–6″
between coupler pulling faces	57′–2–1/2″
Fuel capacity	1,200 gals.
Speed	92 mph.
Builder	ALCO

(Courtesy of G. W. Hockaday.)

RS36

Norfolk and Western No. 2870 is an RS36, and 1,800 hp. ALCO locomotive. The N&W owns eleven of them. It is a road switcher shown here switching cars in the Bison yard in Buffalo. (Photo by author.)

Delaware and Hudson No. 5015, RS36, ALCO road switcher with experimental paint scheme. (Courtesy of George W. Hockaday, Delaware and Hudson Railroad.)

RSD4

Central Railroad of New Jersey No. 1604, ALCO RSD4. This is a heavy-duty, six-axle road switcher near Allentown, Pennsylvania. (Courtesy of John B. Egan.)

RSD5

Penn Central RSD5, No. 6800, southbound pulling a train into the yards near Penn Central Terminal in Buffalo, New York. (Photo by author.)

ALCO RSD5, No. 2150, heavy-duty road switcher rated at 1,600 hp. (Courtesy of the Milwaukee Road.)

RSD12

No. 6862, an RSD12, of the Penn Central, is another road switcher for which ALCO was famous. This 1,800 hp. model is shown here shortly after receiving a new paint job. (Photo by author.)

Horsepower	1,800
Engine	1 – 12 cylinder V
	Model 251
Main Generator	1 GE Model GT586
Traction Motors	6 GE Model 752
Wheels	40"
Air Brakes	26L
Wheel Base	
each truck	12'–6"
truck centers	31'–9"
Maximum Dimensions	
height	14'–6"
between coupler pulling faces	58'–1–3/4"
Fuel capacity	1,200 gals.
Speed	80 mph.
Builder	ALCO

(Courtesy of S. S. Lingenfelter.)

RSD15

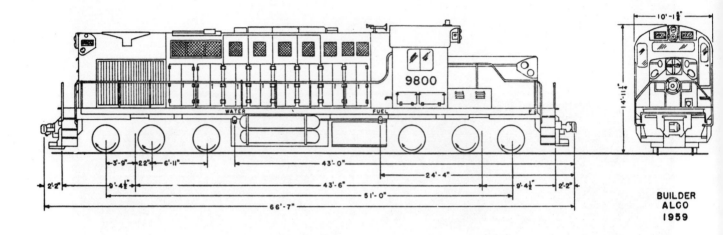

BUILDER
ALCO
1959

Horsepower	2,400
Engine	1 – 16 cylinder V
	Model 251
Main Generator	1 GE Model GT 586
Traction Motors	6 GE Model GT 752
Wheels	40″
Air Brakes	24RL
Wheel Base	
each truck	12′–6″
truck centers	38′–6″
Maximum Dimensions	
height	14′–8–3/8″
between coupler pulling faces	66′–7″
Fuel capacity	1,350 gals.
Speed	80 mph.
Builder	ALCO

(Courtesy of Atchison, Topeka, and Santa Fe Railroad.)

3

GENERAL-PURPOSE LOCOMOTIVES

Grouped by manufacturer in the approximate
order of their appearance on American railroads.

GP7

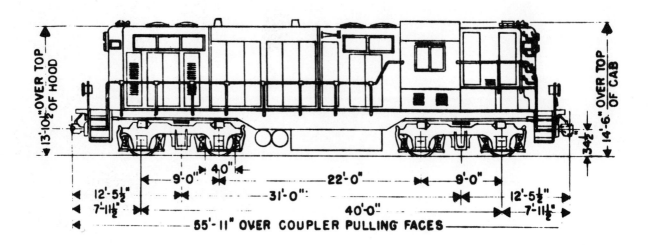

Horsepower	1500
Engine	1 – 16 cylinder
	EMD Model 567
Main Generator	1 EMD Model D12B
Traction Motors	4 EMD Model D27
Wheels	40″
Air Brakes	6BL
Wheel Base	
each truck	9′–0″
truck centers	31′–0″
locomotive	40′–0″
Maximum Dimensions	
width	10′–3″
height	14′–6″
between coupler pulling faces	55′–11″
Fuel capacity	800 gal.
Speed	55 mph.
Builder	EMD

(Courtesy of G. P. Barth)

GP7

Erie-Lackawanna GP7, No. 1226, taking a breather from its yard work at Tonawanda yards in Tonawanda, New York. It is a 1,500 hp. locomotive built by EMD (Electro-Motive Division of General Motors). (Photo by author.)

Toronto, Hamilton, and Buffalo GP7, No. 76, in Penn Central yards in Niagara Falls, New York. The TH&B regularly pulls freight across the international border to the United States and picks up freight for Canada. (Photo by author.)

Baltimore and Ohio GP7, No. 5626, speeding past Beaver, Pennsylvania; behind is a Baltimore and Ohio SD40, No. 7598. (Photo by author.)

A determined column of Chicago and Northwestern GP7s hauling a fast freight train. (Courtesy of Chicago and Northwestern Railroad.)

GP7

Frisco GP7, No. 581, bedecked with flags. (Courtesy of Saint Louis and San Francisco Railroad.)

Penn Central No. 5889, GP7, waits for its turn to switch cars at Center Street (New York Central junction) in Youngstown, Ohio. (Photo by author.)

GP9

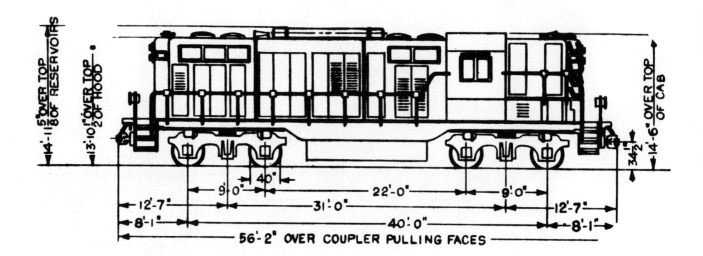

Horsepower	1,750
Engine	1 – 16 cylinder
	EMD Model 567
Main Generator	1 EMD Model D12B
Traction Motors	4 EMD Model D37
Wheels	40″
Air Brakes	6BL
Wheel base	
each truck	9′–0″
truck centers	31′–0″
locomotive	40′–0″
Maximum Dimensions	
width	10′–3″
height	14′–11–5/8″
between coupler pulling faces	56′–2″
Fuel capacity	800 gals.
Speed	55 mph.
Builder	EMD

(Courtesy of G. P. Barth)

GP9

Baltimore and Ohio GP9 just coming out of the fueling station in New Castle, Pennsylvania yards. No. 5958 works as a yard engine in New Castle. In the background is the Pittsburgh and Lake Erie Railroad mainline to Pittsburgh, Pennsylvania. (Photo by author.)

Grand Trunk Western (part of the Canadian National System) stopped in the Fort Erie, Ontario, yards. This GP9, No. 4428, picked up some snow on its way into Fort Erie from eastern Canada. (Photo by author.)

GP9

No. 30 of the Western Maryland Railroad is an un-usual GP9. It has its nose cut down making it take on the appearance of a GP20. (Courtesy of Western Maryland Railroad.)

Denver and Rio Grande Western GP9, No. 5942, switching cars in Denver, Colorado. (Courtesy of John E. Green.)

GP9

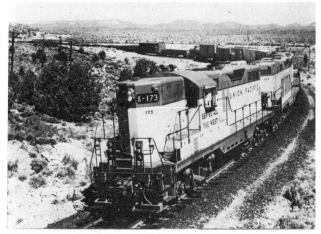

Union Pacific GP9, X–173, with GP9 B-units, pulls a twisting train over the desert at Crestline, Nevada. (Courtesy of Union Pacific Railroad.)

Chesapeake and Ohio GP9, No. 5972, in the Erie-Lackawanna yards in Buffalo, New York. (Photo by author.)

Chicago and Northwestern GP9s, Nos. 1749 and 1760, hitting the mainline. (Courtesy of Chicago and Northwestern Railroad.)

GP9B

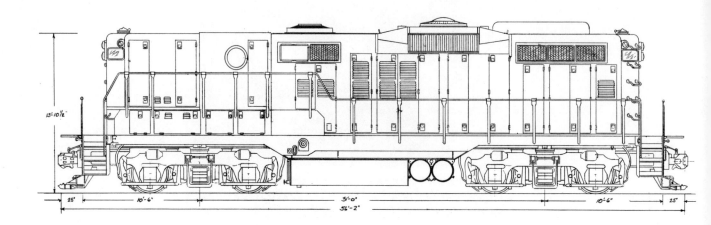

Horsepower	1,750
Engine	1 – 16 cylinder
Main Generator	1 Model D12B
Traction Motors	4 Model D37
Wheels	40″
Air Brakes	24RL
Wheel Base	
each truck	9′
truck centers	31′
Maximum Dimensions	
height	14′–6″
between coupler pulling faces	56′–2″
Fuel capacity	800 gals.
Speed	89 mph.
Builder	EMD

(Courtesy of
Electro-Motive Division of General Motors Corporation.)

GP9B

No. 150B, 1,750 hp. auxillary locomotive, in Denver, Colorado. Except for not having a cab, this locomotive looks like any other GP9. (Courtesy of John E. Green.)

GP18

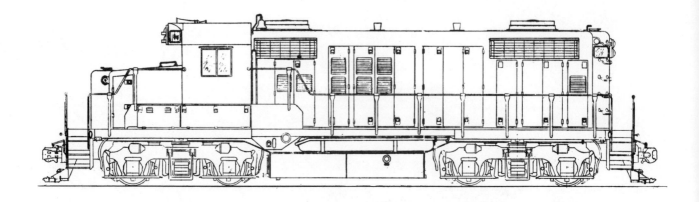

Horsepower	1,800
Engine	1 – 16 cylinder
Main Generator	1 Model D22
Traction Motors	4 Model D47
Wheels	40″
Air Brakes	26L
Wheel Base	
each truck	9′
truck centers	31′
Maximum Dimensions	
height	15′–3/16″
between coupler pulling faces	56′–2″
Fuel capacity	900 gals.
Speed	89 mph.
Builder	EMD

(Courtesy of
Electro-Motive Division of General Motors Corporation.)

GP18

No. 460, a GP18, an 1,800 hp. road switcher, is one of five such locomotives owned by the Louisville and Nashville Railroad. (Courtesy of Louisville and Nashville Railroad.)

GP20

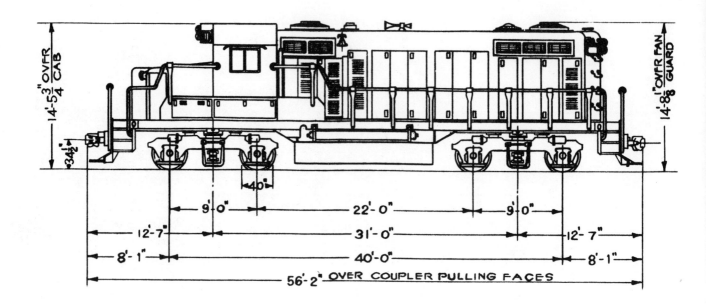

Horsepower	2,000
Engine	1 – 16 cylinder V
Main Generator	1 EMD Model D–22 Direct Drive
Traction Motors	4 EMD Model D67
Wheels	40"
Air Brakes	26L
Wheel Base	
each truck	9'
truck centers	31'
Maximum Dimensions	
height	14'–8–1/8"
between coupler pulling faces	56'–2"
Fuel capacity	2,350 gal.
Speed	71 mph.
Builder	EMD

(Courtesy of S. S. Lingenfelter.)

GP20

Union Pacific Nos. 714, 727, and 701, GP20s, pulling Pacific Fruit Express refrigerator cars past 134th Street crossing in Omaha, Nebraska. (Courtesy of Union Pacific Railroad.)

GP30

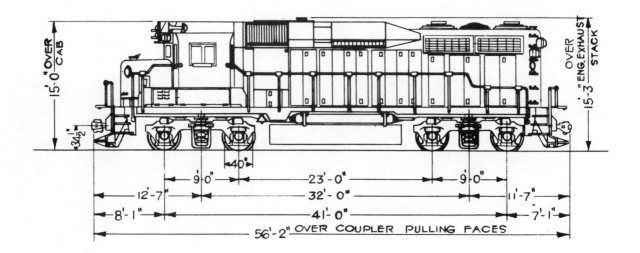

Horsepower	2,250
Engine	1 – 16 cylinder
	EMD Model 16–567 D3
Main Generator	1 EMD Model D22–DT
Traction Motors	4 EMD D57–B–1
Wheels	40″
Wheel Base	
each truck	9′–0″
truck centers	32′–0″
locomotive	41′–0″
Maximum Dimensions	
height	15′–3″
between coupler pulling faces	56′–2″
Fuel capacity	1,700 gal.
Speed	83 mph.
Builder	EMD

(Courtesy of S. S. Lingenfelter.)

GP30

Penn Central GP30, No. 2199, following an SD40 in a
freight train headed south toward Pittsburgh after
leaving Conway yards. (Photo by author.)

No. 6955, Baltimore and Ohio GP30, sits patiently
waiting a turn at the fuel station in New Castle,
Pennsylvania. No. 4028 behind No. 6955 is a B&O
GP40. (Photo by author.)

GP30

Chesapeake and Ohio No. 3009, GP30, nestled in amongst the Erie-Lackawanna locomotives in the Bison yards, Buffalo, New York. The Erie-Lackawanna, Chessie System, and Norfolk and Western Railroads all use the Bison yard. (Photo by author.)

Kansas City Southern GP30, No. 109, in former paint scheme. (Photo by Harold K. Vollrath; courtesy of Kansas City Southern Railroad.)

GP30

Union Pacific GP30, No. 718, taken when it was in its youth. (Courtesy of Union Pacific Railroad.)

Chicago and Northwestern GP30s No. 817 and No. 812 handling mainline traffic. Each is a 2,250 hp. locomotive. (Courtesy of Chicago and Northwestern Railroad.)

GP35

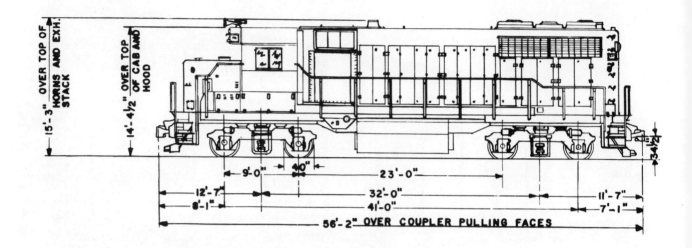

Horsepower		2,500
Engine		1 – 16 cylinder
		EMD Model 16–567 D3A
Main Generator		1 EMD Model D32
Traction Motors		4 EMD Model D–67
Wheels		40″
Wheel Base		
	each truck	9′–0″
	truck centers	32′–0″
locomotive		41′–0″
Maximum Dimensions		
	height	15′–3″
	between coupler pulling faces	56′–2″
Fuel capacity		1,700 gal.
Speed		83 mph.
Builder		EMD

(Courtesy of S. S. Lingenfelter.)

GP35

**Canadian Pacific (CP Rail) GP35, No. 5024, coupled
in line waiting to be fueled in Toronto yard.** (Photo
by author.)

**Missouri Pacific (MoPac) Lines Nos. 600 and 601
GP35s.** (Courtesy of Missouri Pacific Railroad.)

GP35

Erie-Lackawanna GP35, No. 2555, (behind an E8; a passenger locomotive) helps pull coal hoppers out of Youngstown, Ohio. (Photo by author.)

A pair of Chicago and Northwestern GP35s with GP30 sandwiched in between. (Courtesy of Chicago and Northwestern Railroad.)

GP35

Penn Central GP35 No. 2338, awaiting its turn for refueling in Conway yards near East Conway, Pennsylvania. (Photo by author.)

Denver and Rio Grande No. 3035, GP35, pulling into Denver yards. (Courtesy of John E. Green.)

GP38

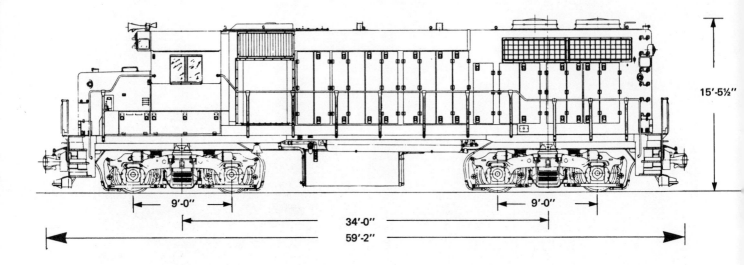

Horsepower	2,000
Engine	1 – 16 cylinder V
	EMD Model 16–645–E
Main Generator	1 EMD Model D32
Traction Motors	4 EMD Model D77
Wheels	40″
Air Brakes	26L
Wheel Base	
each truck	9′
truck centers	34′
Maximum Dimensions	
height	15′–5–1/2″
between coupler pulling faces	59′–2″
Fuel capacity	3,600 gals.
Speed	70 mph.
Builder	EMD

(Courtesy of
Electro-Motive Division of General Motors Corporation.)

GP38

Louisville and Nashville GP38, No. 4035, posing in its new paint job. (Courtesy of Louisville and Nashville Railroad.)

GP38

The deadpan expression of the front of the GP38 as typified here by Santa Fe No. 3517. This is a 2,000 hp. general-purpose locomotive. (Courtesy of Atchison, Topeka, and Santa Fe Railroad.)

GP38

Penn Central, No. 7744, GP38, with No. 7742, passing under the Center Street Bridge in Youngstown, Ohio. (Photo by author.)

Baltimore and Ohio (part of the Chessie System) No. 3812, GP38, pulling a string of coal cars past Republic Steel in Youngstown, Ohio. (Photo by author.)

GP38–2

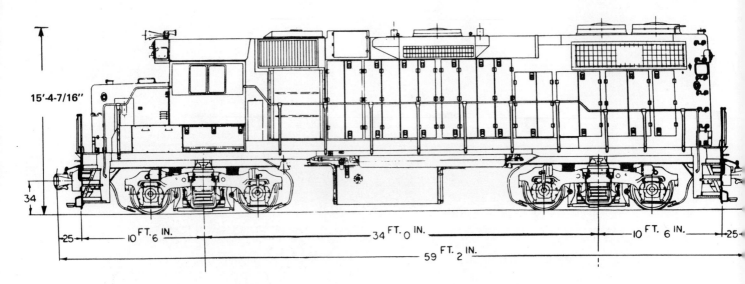

Horsepower	2,000
Engine	1 – 16 cylinder
Main Generator (Alternator)	1 Model AR10–D14
Traction Motors	4 Model D77
Wheels	40″
Air Brakes	26L
Wheel Base	
each truck	9′
truck centers	34′
Maximum Dimensions	
height	15′–4–7/16″
between coupler pulling faces	59′–2″
Fuel capacity	1,700 gals.
Speed	82 mph.
Builder	EMD

(Courtesy of
Electro-Motive Division of General Motors Corporation.)

GP38–2

Lehigh Valley GP38-2, No. 317, pulling up for a crew change near the Bison yard of the Erie-Lackawanna, Norfolk and Western. The GP38-2 is essentially a GP38, a 2,000 hp. road switcher, except that it has a main alternator for producing electric current instead of a generator. GP38-2 models went into production in 1972. (Photo by author.)

Penn Central GP38-2, with an SD45 following, pull into Conway yards. The GP38-2, bno. 8099, is a 2,000 hp. general-purpose locomotive. (Photo by author.)

GP40

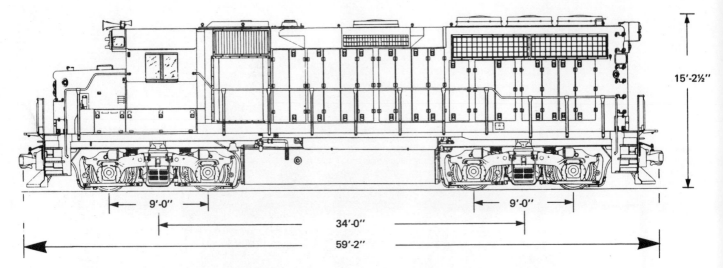

Horsepower	3,000
Engine	1 – 16 cylinder V GM Model 16–645–E
Main Generator	1 EMD Model D32
Traction Motors	4 EMD Model D77
Wheels	40"
Air Brakes	26L
Wheel Base	
each truck	9'
truck centers	34'
Maximum Dimensions	
height	15'–2–1/2"
between coupler pulling faces	59'–2"
Fuel capacity	3,600 gals.
Speed	71 mph.
Builder	EMD

(Courtesy of
Electro-Motive Division of General Motors Corporation.)

GP40

Cotton Belt GP40, No. 7601, eastbound on Penn Central through Buffalo, New York. (Photo by author.)

Seaboard Coast Line GP40, No. 1566, freshly delivered to the railroad from EMD. (Courtesy of Seaboard Coast Line.)

GP40

Western Pacific Nos. 3523, 3532, and 3517, all GP40s, lead Western Pacific All-Container train that operates daily between Oakland, California, and Salt Lake City, Utah, to connect with the Union Pacific and Denver and Rio Grande Western. This is the Clio Bridge, first used by this train in July of 1973. (Courtesy of Western Pacific Railroad.)

GP40

GP40, No. 3214, Penn Central general-purpose locomotive followed by No. 2193, GP30, stopped on the mainline awaiting signal to proceed to Frontier yards in Buffalo. (Photo by author.)

Baltimore and Ohio GP40, No. 4028, pulling a freight train through New Castle, Pennsylvania. (Photo by author.)

GP40–2

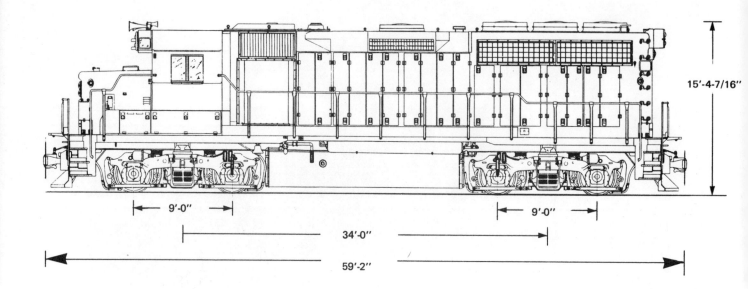

Horsepower	3,000
Engine	1 – 16 cylinder
Main Generator (Alternator)	1 Model AR10–D14
Traction Motors	4 Model D77
Wheels	40″
Air Brakes	26L
Wheel Base	
each truck	9′
truck centers	34′
Maximum Dimensions	
height	15′–4–7/16″
between coupler pulling faces	59′–2″
Fuel capacity	2,600 gals.
Speed	82 mph.
Builder	EMD

(Courtesy of
Electro-Motive Division of General Motors Corporation.)

GP40–2

Baltimore and Ohio GP40-2, No. 4122, pulling into New Castle, Pennsylvania, yards with a GP40, No. 3758, behind it. (Photo by author.)

4

SPECIAL-DUTY LOCOMOTIVES

Grouped by manufacturer in the approximate
order of their appearance on American railroads.

SD7

Bessemer and Lake Erie No. 451, and SD7, switching a train of loaded coal hoppers. The SD7 is a six-axle, heavy-duty 1,500 hp. road switcher. The Bessemer and Lake Erie hauls heavy loads of iron ore and coal and most of its locomotives are six-axle models that offer higher traction than four-axle locomotives. No. 451 is pictured here in Greenville, Pennsylvania. (Photo by author.)

Horsepower	1,500
Engine	1 – 16 cylinder
Main Generator	1 Model D12C
Traction Motors	6 Model D27
Wheels	40″
Air Brakes	24RL
Wheel Base	
each truck	13′–7″
truck centers	35′
Maximum Dimensions	
height	15′
between coupler pulling faces	60′–8″
Fuel capacity	2,400 gals.
Speed	65 mph.
Builder	EMD

(Courtesy of
Electro-Motive Division of General Motors Corporation.)

SD9

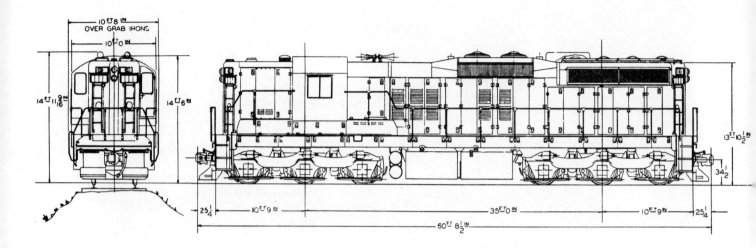

Horsepower	1,750
Engine	1 – 16 cylinder V
Main Generator	1 – D12
Traction Motors	6
Wheels	40″
Air Brakes	6BL
Wheel Base	
each truck	13′–7″
truck centers	35′
Maximum Dimensions	
height	14′–6″
between coupler pulling faces	60′–8–1/2″
Fuel capacity	1,200 gals.
Speed	89 mph.
Builder	EMD

(Courtesy of
Electro-Motive Division of General Motors Corporation)

SD9

Bessemer and Lake Erie Railroad Nos. 829 and 830 spending a quiet weekend at the Greenville, Pennsylvania, shops. The SD9 is the larger brother of the EMD GP9. It has six driving axles and is well suited to hauling the heavy coal and ore loads the Bessemer specializes in handling. (Photo by author.)

Colorado and Southern (part of the Burlington Northern) No. 831, an SD9, in Denver, Colorado. (Courtesy of John E. Green.)

SD24

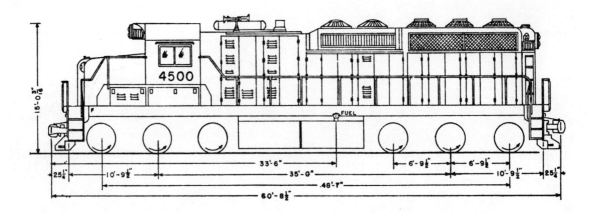

Horsepower	2,400
Engine	1 – 16 cylinder
Main Generator	1 Model D22
Traction Motors	6 Model D47
Wheels	40″
Air Brakes	26L
Wheel Base	
each truck	13′–7″
truck centers	35′
Maximum Dimensions	
height	15′–1″
between coupler pulling faces	60′–8″
Fuel capacity	1,200 gals.
Speed	89 mph.
Builder	EMD

(Courtesy of Atchison, Topeka, and Santa Fe Railroad.)

SD24

Union Pacific No. 422, SD24, with four SD24–Bs.
(Courtesy of Union Pacific Railroad.)

SD35

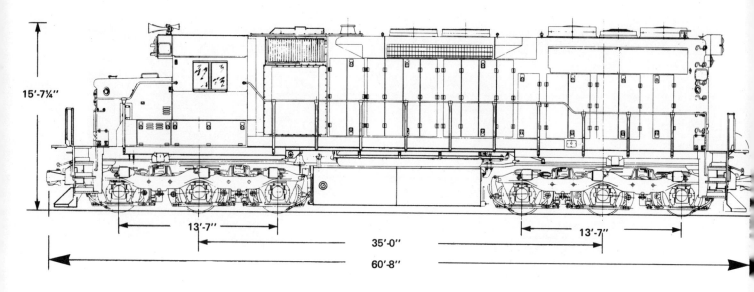

Horsepower	2,500
Engine	1 – 16 cylinder V Model 56TD3A
Main Generator	1 EMD Model D32
Traction Motors	6 EMD Model D67
Wheels	40″
Air Brakes	26L
Wheel Base	
each truck	13′–7″
truck centers	35′
Maximum Dimensions	
height	15′–7–1/4″
between coupler pulling faces	60′–8″
Fuel capacity	3,000 gals.
Speed	83 mph.
Builder	EMD

(Courtesy of
Electro-Motive Division of General Motors Corporation.)

SD35

Penn Central SD35, No. 6000, inching its way east-bound through Conway yards in Freedom, Pennsylvania. (Photo by author.)

SD35

No. 1901, SD35, of the Seaboard Coast Line. The SD35 is the slightly larger brother of the GP35 and has six axles driving instead of the GP35s four axles. (Courtesy of Seaboard Coast Line.)

Much besmudged No. 7425 of the Chesapeake and Ohio (Chessie System). This SD35 was helping to pull coal into Youngstown, Ohio. (Photo by author.)

SD35

Western Maryland No.7433, SD35, at the round-house. (Courtesy of Western Maryland Railroad.)

Baltimore and Ohio SD35, No. 7413, westbound with a freight train out of Youngstown, Ohio. (Photo by author.)

SD38

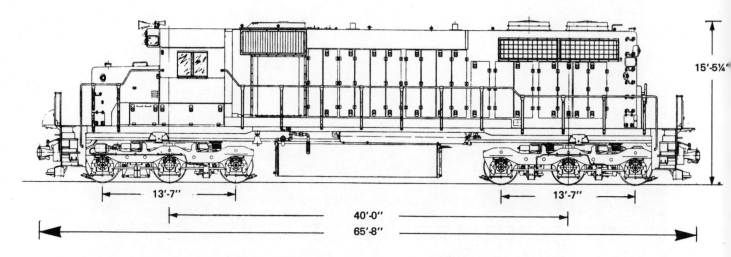

Horsepower	2,000
Engine	1 – 16 cylinder V
	Model 16–645–E
Main Generator	1 EMD Model D32
Traction Motors	6 EMD Model D77
Wheels	40″
Air Brakes	26L
Wheel Base	
each truck	13′–7″
truck centers	40′
Maximum Dimensions	
height	15′–5–1/4″
between coupler pulling faces	65′–8″
Fuel capacity	4,000 gals.
Speed	82 mph.
Builder	EMD

(Courtesy of
Electro-Motive Division of General Motors Corporation.)

SD38

Penn Central SD38, switching cars in Conway yards. SD stands for Special Duty. It is a 2,000 hp. six-axle, heavy-duty road switcher. By adding the fifth and sixth axles, the tractive ability of this and other locomotives is increased. (Photo by author.)

SD38–2

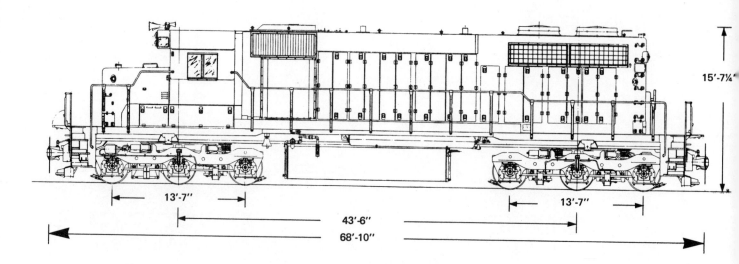

Horsepower	2,000
Engine	1 – 16 cylinder
Main Generator (Alternator)	1 AR10–D14
Traction Motors	6 Model D77
Wheels	40"
Air Brakes	26L
Wheel Base	
each truck	13'–7"
truck centers	43'–6"
Maximum Dimensions	
height	15'–7–¼"
between coupler pulling faces	68'–10"
Fuel capacity	3,200 gals.
Speed	82 mph.
Builder	EMD

(Courtesy of
Electro-Motive Division of General Motors Corporation.)

SD39

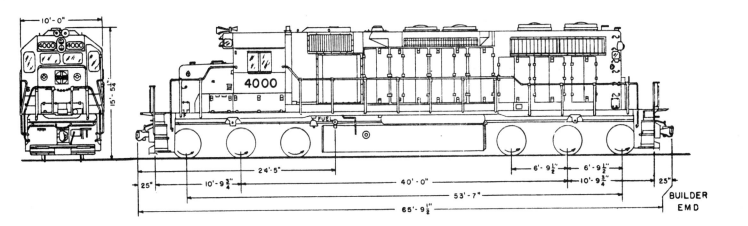

Horsepower	2,300
Engine	1 – 12 cylinder
	EMD Model 12–645 E3
Main Generator	1 EMD Model D32–E
Traction Motors	6 D77
Wheels	40″
Air Brakes	26L
Wheel Base	
each truck	13′–7″
truck centers	40′
Maximum Dimensions	
height	15′–5–1/4″
between coupler pulling faces	65′–9–1/2″
Fuel capacity	4,000 gals.
Builder	EMD

(Courtesy of Atchison, Topeka, and Santa Fe Railroad.)

SD40

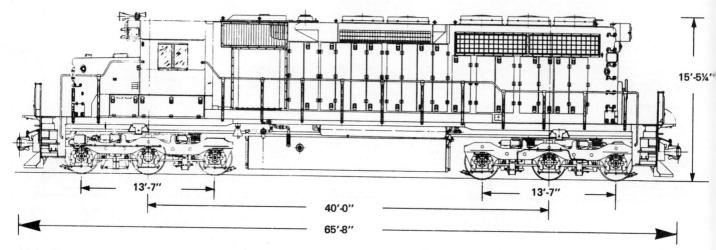

Horsepower	3,000
Engine	1–16 cylinder
	EMD Model 16 –645E
Main Generator	1 EMD Model AR–10
	alternator
Traction Motors	6 EMD Model D–77
Wheels	40″
Air Brakes	26L
Wheel Base	
each truck	13′–7″
truck centers	40′–0″
locomotive	53′–7″
Maximum Dimensions	
height	15′–5–1/4″
between coupler pulling faces	65′–8″
Weight, fully loaded	180 tons
Fuel capacity	4,000 gal.
Speed	72 mph.
Builder	EMD

(Courtesy of
Electro-Motive Division of General Motors Corporation.)

SD40

SD40, No. 6050, of the Penn Central leaves Conway yard helping to pull a westbound freight train. The SD40 is a 3,000 hp., special-duty, six-axle locomotive built by EMD of General Motors. The Penn Central SD40s are numbered 6040–6104 and 6240–6284.
(Photo by author.)

SD40

Front view of Union Pacific SD40, No. 3041, a 3,000 hp. road locomotive. (Courtesy of Union Pacific Railroad.)

CP Rail No. 5502, SD40, waits in Toronto yards for refueling. (Photo by author.)

SD40

Western Maryland No. 7473, SD40, shines in the snow. (Courtesy of Western Maryland Railroad.)

Southern Pacific SD40, No. 8402, hooked in with Penn Central road locomotives in Conway yards, north of Pittsburgh, Pennsylvania. (Photo by author.)

SD40–2

Union Pacific Nos. 3124, 3131, 3139, and 3136, SD40–2 diesels, passing a hot-box detector in Nebraska. The SD40–2 is part of a new generation of diesels whose main generator has been replaced by an alternator. (Courtesy of Union Pacific Railroad.)

Horsepower	3,000
Engine	1 – 16 cylinder
Main Generator (Alternator)	1 Model AR10–D14
Traction Motors	6 Model D77
Wheels	40"
Air Brakes	26L
Wheel Base	
each truck	13"–7"
truck centers	43'–6"
Maximum Dimensions	
height	15'–7–3/16"
between coupler pulling faces	68'–10"
Fuel capacity	3,200 gals.
Speed	82 mph.
Builder	EMD.

(Courtesy of Union Pacific Railroad.)

SD45

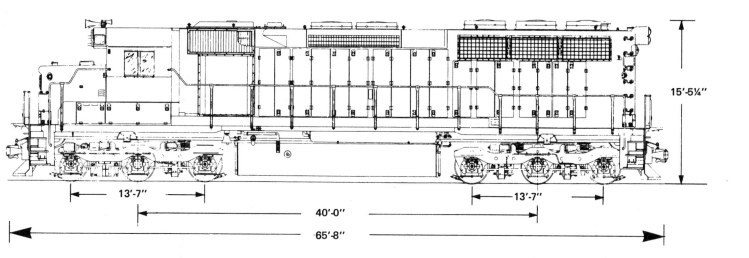

Horsepower	3,600
Engine	1 – 20 cylinder V 20–645E
Main Generator (Alternator)	1 EMD Model AR–10
Traction Motors	6 EMD Model D77
Wheels	40″
Air Brakes	26L
Wheel Base	
each truck	13′–7″
truck centers	40′
Maximum Dimensions	
height	15′–5–1/4″
between coupler pulling faces	65′–8″
Fuel capacity	4,000 gals.
Speed	82 mph.
Builder	EMD

(Courtesy of
Electro-Motive Division of General Motors Corporation.)

SD45

Chicago and Northwestern SD45, No. 956, along the Illinois Division. (Courtesy of Chicago and Northwestern Railroad.)

Erie-Lackawanna, SD45, No. 3606, behind ALCO C425, No. 2459, awaiting refueling in Bison yards, Buffalo, New York. The locomotive only partially in view to the right is an SDP45. (Photo by author.)

SD45

No. 9066, Cotton Belt SD45 running on the Baltimore and Ohio through New Castle, Pennsylvania. (Photo by author.)

Burlington Northern No. 6430, a 3,600 hp. SD45, doing some switching in Denver, Colorado. The SD45 has a twenty-cylinder diesel, the largest diesel engine on American railroads. (Courtesy of John E. Green.)

SD45

Frisco SD45, No. 907, posing in its new paint job. The Saint Louis and San Francisco Railroad Company (Frisco) owns forty-nine SD45s. (Courtesy of Saint Louis and San Francisco Railroad.)

SD45–2

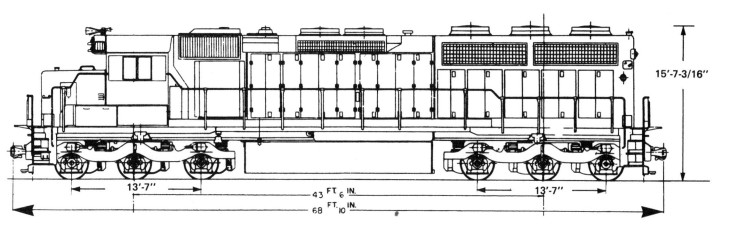

Horsepower	3,600
Engine	1 – 20 cylinder
Main Generator (Alternator)	1 Model AR10–D14
Traction Motors	6 Model D77
Wheels	40″
Air Brakes	26L
Wheel Base	
each truck	13′–7″
truck centers	43′–6″
Maximum Dimensions	
height	15′–7–3/16″
between coupler pulling faces	68′–10″
Fuel capacity	3,200 gals.
Speed	82 mph.
Builder	EMD

(Courtesy of
Electro-Motive Division of General Motors Corporation.)

SD45–2

Santa Fe SD45-2, the newer model SD45 (with main alternator instead of main generator), No. 5695. The SD45-2 lacks the big elephant ears in the back that the SD45 has. (Courtesy of Atchison, Topeka, and Santa Fe Railroad.)

SD45T-2

No. 9308, Southern Pacific SD45T-2, is a special elongated SD45-2 that has air intakes lower on the carbody to enable the engine to get fresh air more easily in tunnels. "T" stands for tunnel. The radiators are on the top of the locomotive and air is forced up through them. This helps to handle the problem with normal locomotives overheating and starving for air in tunnels. This locomotive is seen here in Denver, Colorado. (Courtesy of John E. Green.)

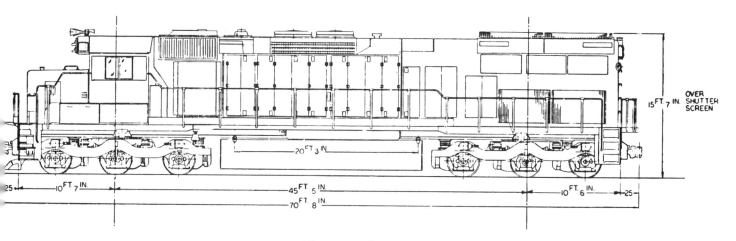

(Courtesy of
Electro-Motive Division of General Motors Corporation.)

5

PASSENGER LOCOMOTIVES

Grouped by manufacturer in the approximate
order of their appearance on American railroads.

PA1

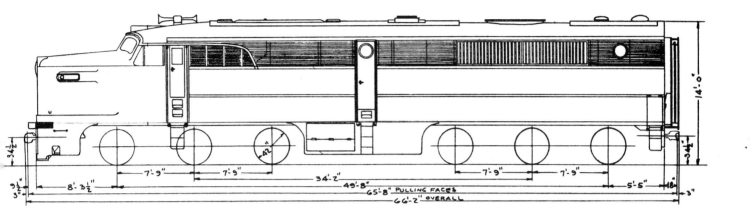

Horsepower	2,000
Engine	1 – 16 cylinder
Main Generator	1 GE Model 5GT 566
Traction Motors	4
Wheels	42″
Air Brakes	24 RL
Wheel Base	
each truck	15′–6″
truck centers	34′–2″
Maximum Dimensions	
height	14′
between coupler pulling faces	65′–8″
Fuel capacity	1,260 gals.
Speed	104 mph.
Builder	ALCO

(Courtesy of G. W. Hockaday.)

PA1

No. 19, one of the highly dashing PA1s built by ALCO. The PA1 was a passenger locomotive. The Delaware and Hudson owns the last four PA1 in existence, making this an endangered species. The railroad had been using them for excursion trains, but, with the reinstatement of passenger service from Albany to Montreal, the four again will be pulling the passenger trains. All four are scheduled to be completely rebuilt. (Courtesy of George W. Hockaday; Delaware and Hudson Railroad.)

E7A

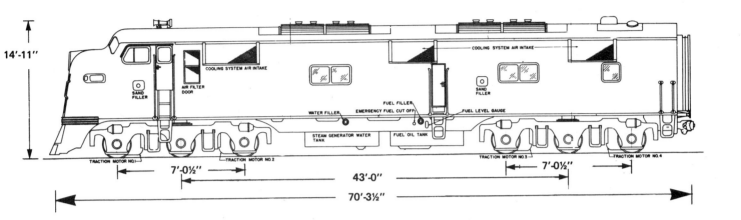

Horsepower	2,000
Engine	2 – 12 cylinder V
	GM Model 567
Main Generator	2 EMD Model D4D
	Direct Drive
Traction Motors	4 EMD Model D7, D17
	or D27
Wheels	36″
Air Brakes	24RL
Wheel Base	
each truck	7′–0–1/2″
truck centers	43′
Maximum Dimensions	
height	14′–11″
between coupler pulling faces	70′–3–1/2″
Fuel capacity	1,200 gals.
Speed	98 mph.
Builder	EMD

(Courtesy of
Electro-Motive Division of General Motors Corporation.)

E7A

Former Boston and Maine E7A, sold to and repainted for Kansas City Southern. No. 6 is shown here enroute to delivery to the Kansas City Southern. (Courtesy of John B. Egan.)

Former New York Central, now Penn Central, E7A, No. 4025, now used in freight service, stopping in Rochester, New York, before continuing west to Buffalo. (Photo by author.)

E7B

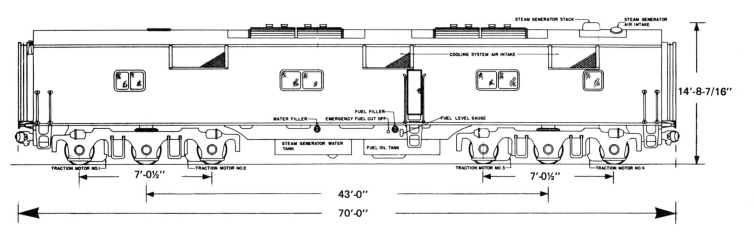

Horsepower	2,000
Engine	2 – 12 cylinder V
	GM Model 567
main Generator	2 EMD Model D4D
	Direct Drive
Traction Motors	4 EMD Model D–7F 600V
	or D17, D27
Wheels	36″
Air Brakes	24RL
Wheel Base	
each truck	7′–0½″
truck centers	43′
Maximum Dimensions	
height	14′–8–7/16″
between coupler pulling faces	70′
Fuel capacity	1,200 gals.
Speed	98 mph.
Builder	EMD

(Courtesy of
Electro-Motive Division of General Motors Corporation.)

E7B

Ex-New York Central No. 4111, E7B, this locomotive was originally a passenger locomotive, but is now used in freight service. The Penn Central only lists three of these locomotives on its roster and they most likely will not last long. (Photo by author.)

E8A

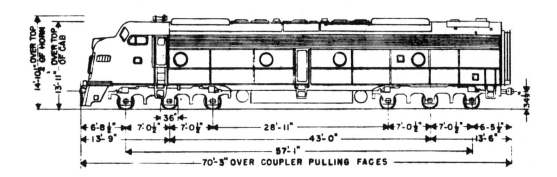

Horsepower	2,250
Engine	2 – 12 cylinder V
	GM 567B
Main Generator	2 EMD Model D–15B
Traction Motors	4 EMD Model D–27
Wheels	36″
Air Brakes	24Rʟ
Wheel Base	
each truck	7′–0–1/2″
truck centers	43′–1″
Maximum Dimensions	
height	14′–10–1/2″
between coupler pulling faces	70′–3″
Fuel capacity	1,200 gals.
Speed	98 mph.
Builder	EMD

(Courtesy of G. P. Barth.)

E8A

Canadian Pacific No. 1800, E8A, in former paint scheme. (Courtesy of Canadian Pacific Railroad.)

Union Pacific No. 940, E8A, passenger locomotive. (Courtesy of Union Pacific Railroad.)

E8A

Penn Central No. 259 E8A, former Penn Central (and New York Central) No. 4059, ready to depart for New York with the early afternoon Amtrak passenger train. This is a growing spectator function as well, with the engineer, not shown, giving lectures to the visitors on railroading. (Photo by author.)

E8A

Chicago and Northwestern No. 507, E8A, purchased from Union Pacific and rebuilt at Oelwein, pushes its first commuter train into Chicago Terminal. F7B coupled to it was for additional power. (Courtesy of Chicago and Northwestern Railroad.)

Erie-Lackawanna E8A, No. 829, basking in the summer sun in Youngstown, Ohio. The Erie-Lackawanna uses these passenger locomotives for freight and commuter traffic. (Photo by author.)

E8B

This is a very uncommon E8B unit. It is one of six former Union Pacific E8Bs, rebuilt, and equipped with a cab by the Chicago and Northwestern at Oelwein. No. 504 is seen here pulling a commuter train in a test run from Northwestern Station in Chicago. (Courtesy of Chicago and Northwestern Railroad.)

E9A

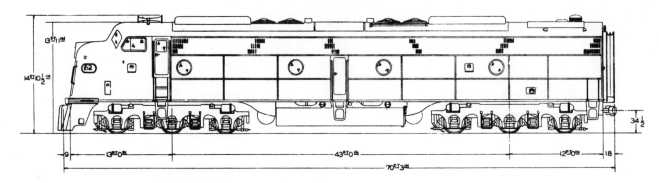

Horsepower	2,400
Engine	2 – 12 cylinder V
	GM 567C
Main Generator	2 – EMD D15B
Traction Motors	4 – EMD D37
Wheels	40"
Air Brakes	24RL
Wheel Base	
each truck	14'–1"
truck centers	43"
Maximum Dimensions	
height	14'–10–1/2"
between coupler pulling faces	70'–3"
Fuel capacity	1,200 gals.
Speed	117 mph.
Builder	EMD

(Courtesy of
Electro-Motive Division of General Motors Corporation.)

Milwaukee Road E9A, No. 33C (Courtesy of the Milwaukee Road.)

E9B

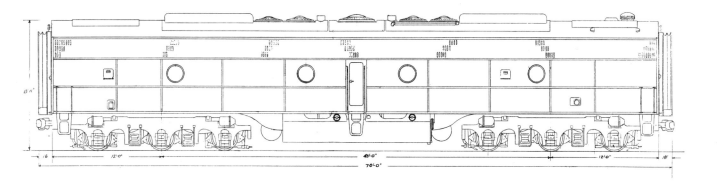

Horsepower	2,400
Engine	2 – 12 cylinder V GM 567C
Main Generator	2 – EMD D15B
Traction Motors	4 – EMD D37
Wheels	40″
Air Brakes	24RL
Wheel Base	
each truck	14′–1″
truck centers	43′
Maximum Dimensions	
height	14′–10–1/2″
between coupler pulling faces	70′
Fuel capacity	1,200 gals.
Speed	90 mph.
Builder	EMD

(Courtesy of
Electro-Motive Division of General Motors Corporation.)

E9B

Union Pacific, 2,400 hp., E9B, auxillary engine No. 950B. (Courtesy of Union Pacific Railroad.)

SDP35

Union Pacific SDP35 (special-duty passenger locomotive) with a steam generator. No. 1400 is a 2,500 hp., freight-passenger locomotive. (Courtesy of Union Pacific Railroad.)

SDP40

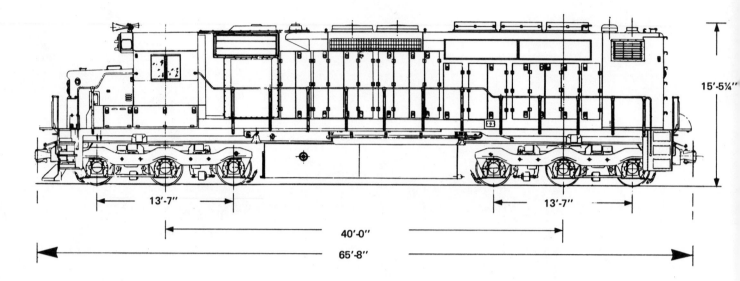

Horsepower	3,000
Engine	1 – 16 cylinder V GM 645 Diesel
Main Generator (Alternator)	1 EMD Model AR–10
Traction Motors	6 EMD Model D77
Wheels	40"
Air Brakes	26L
Wheel Base	
each truck	13'–7"
truck centers	40'
Maximum Dimensions	
height	15'–5–1/4"
between coupler pulling faces	65'–8"
Fuel capacity	3,950 gals.
Speed	89 mph.
Builder	EMD

(Courtesy of
Electro-Motive Division of General Motors Corporation.)

SDP45

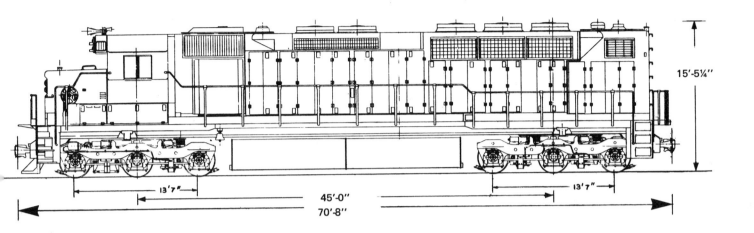

Horsepower	3,600
Engine	1 – 20 cylinder
Main Generator (Alternator)	1 Model AR10
Traction Motors	6 Model D77
Wheels	40"
Air Brakes	26L
Wheel Base	
each truck	13'–7"
truck centers	45'
Maximum Dimensions	
height	15'–5–1/4"
between coupler pulling faces	70'–8"
Fuel capacity	4,950 gals.
Speed	83 mph.
Builder	EMD

(Courtesy of
Electro-Motive Division of General Motors Corporation.)

SDP45

Erie-Lackawanna SDP45s, Nos. 3643 and 3641 rolling slowly westbound to the Erie-Lackawanna yards in Youngstown, Ohio. These are not standard SDP45s since they do not have steam generators in the rear of the carbody. By purchasing the longer bodied SDP45 frame, the Erie-Lackawanna was able to add larger than normal fuel tanks to the locomotives. (Photo by author.)

FP45

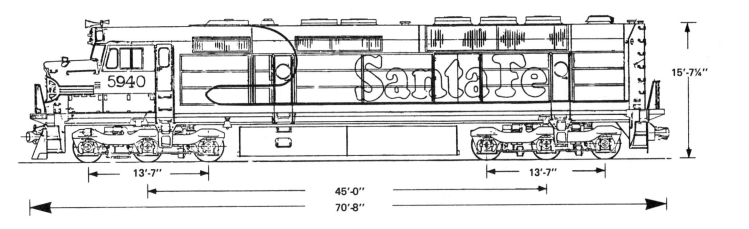

Horsepower	3,600
Engine	1 – 20 cylinder V
	Model 645E3
Main Generator (Alternator)	1 EMD Model AR–10
Traction Motors	6 EMD Model D77
Wheels	40″
Air Brakes	26L
Wheel Base	
each truck	13′–7″
truck centers	45′
Maximum Dimensions	
height	15′–7–1/4″
between coupler pulling faces	70′–8″
Fuel capacity	5,000 gals.
Speed	102 mph.
Builder	EMD

(Courtesy of Atchison, Topeka, and Santa Fe Railroad.)

FP45

The sleek, carbody version of the EMD FP45, 3,600 hp., freight-passenger locomotive No. 3 of the Milwaukee Road. (Courtesy of the Milwaukee Road.)

6

FREIGHT LOCOMOTIVES

Grouped by manufacturer in the approximate
order of their appearance on American railroads.

F3A

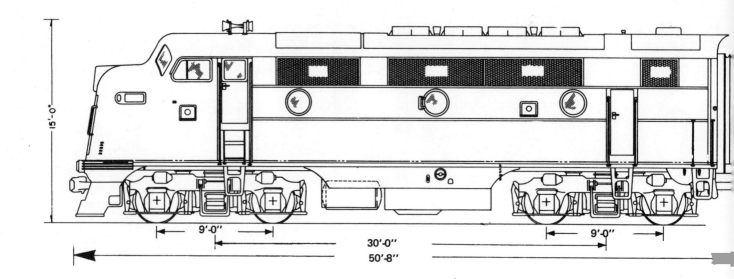

Horsepower	1,500
Engine	1 – 16 cylinder
Main Generator	1 Model D12–D14
Traction Motors	4 Model D7B1
Wheels	40″
Air Brakes	24RL
Wheel Base	
each truck	9′
truck centers	30′
Maximum Dimensions	
height	15′—0″
between coupler pulling faces	50′-8″
Fuel capacity	1,200 gals.
Speed	102 mph.
Builder	EMD

(Courtesy of
Electro-Motive Division of General Motors Corporation.)

F3B

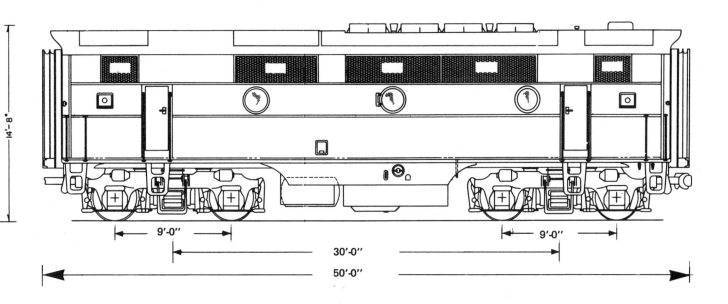

Horsepower	1,500
Engine	1 – 16 cylinder
Main Generator	1 Model D12–D14
Traction Motors	4 Model D7B1
Wheels	40″
Air Brakes	24RL
Wheel Base	
each truck	9′
truck centers	30′
Maximum Dimensions	
height	14′—8″
between coupler pulling faces	50′
Fuel capacity	1,200 gals.
Speed	102 mph.
Builder	EMD

(Courtesy of
Electro-Motive Division of General Motors Corporation.)

F3A and F3B

Erie-Lackawanna F3A, No. 6621, pulling a freight train through North Tonawanda, New York, from Niagara Falls. F3s were built between 1946 and 1949, which makes this an old locomotive. It is still in service, one of the few F3s still around. (Photo by author.)

Kansas City Southern No. 56, F3A, with two F3Bs and another F3A moving without a train. (Courtesy of Kansas City Southern Railroad.)

BL2

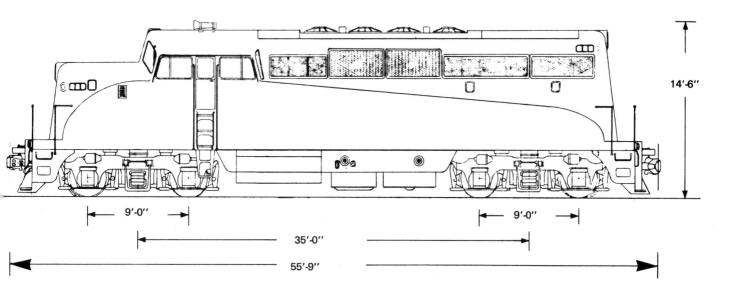

14'-6"

9'-0"   9'-0"

35'-0"

55'-9"

Horsepower	1,500
Engine	1 – 16 cylinder
Main Generator	1 Model D12–D14
Traction Motors	4 Model D27
Wheels	40"
Air Brakes	6 BL or 24 RL
Wheel Base	
each truck	9'
truck centers	35'
Maximum Dimensions	
height	14'–6"
between coupler pulling faces	55'–9"
Fuel capacity	800 gals.
Speed	89 mph.
Builder	EMD

(Courtesy of
Electro-Motive Division of General Motors Corporation.)

BL2

The BL2 is an extremely unusual looking 1,500 hp. locomotive, which could almost pass for a road-freight locomotive, but then again look like a road switcher. The Western Maryland owns two of these, Nos. 81 and 82. They were built in 1948 and considered by the Western Maryland for service as road switchers. Nos. 81 and 82 have no steam generators thereby prohibiting their use in passenger service. They weigh 116 tons each and work on the hump at the Hagerstown, Pennsylvania, yard. (Courtesy of Western Maryland Railroad.)

F7A

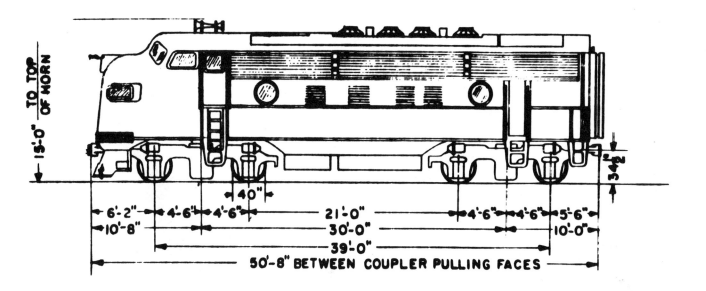

Horsepower	1,500
Engine	1–16 cylinder
	EMD Model 567B
Main Generator	1 EMD Model D12 or D12B
Traction Motors	4 EMD Model D27
Wheels	40″
Air Brakes	24RL
Wheel Base	
each truck	9′–0″
truck centers	30′–0″
locomotive	39′–0″
Maximum Dimensions	
width	10′–7–1/2″
height	15′–0″
between coupler pulling faces	50′–8″
Fuel capacity	1,200 gals.
Speed	65 mph.
Builder	EMD

(Courtesy S. S. Lingenfelter.)

F7A

Baltimore and Ohio No. 4535, F7A unit, backing into the fueling tower in New Castle, Pennsylvania. Behind: No. 4535, F7B unit No. 5420, and a GP9. (Photo by author.)

Pennsylvania (now part of Penn Central) F7A, No. 1482, waiting during switching operations on mainline in Rochester, Pennsylvania. (Photo by author.)

F7A

Western Maryland F7A, No. 242, parked at its roundhouse. (Courtesy of Western Maryland Railroad.)

Missouri Pacific F7A, No. 801, with F7B unit. (Courtesy of Missouri Pacific Railroad.)

F7A

Penn Central F7A, No. 1779, sporting a new paint job. The scene is Conway yards, Freedom, Pennsylvania. No. 1779 is based in Collinwood, Ohio, as can be seen by the name under the numbers on the locomotive. (Photo by author.)

The smiling face of No. 395, Atlantic Coast Line F7A. It has no shortage of headlights. (Courtesy of Seaboard Coast Line/Family Lines System.)

F7B

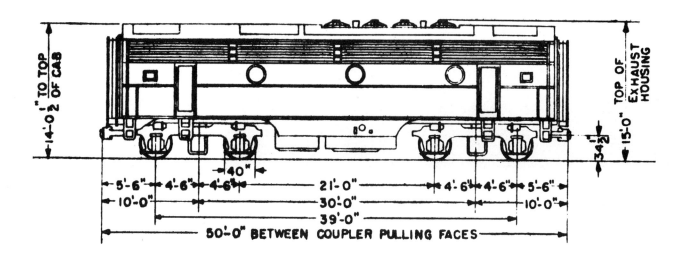

Horsepower	1,500
Engine	1 – 16 cylinder V GM Model 567
Main Generator	1 EMD Model D12 or D12B
Traction Motors	4 EMD Model D27
Wheels	40"
Air Brakes	24RL
Wheel Base	
each truck	9'
truck centers	30'
Maximum Dimensions	
height	15'
between coupler pulling faces	50'
Fuel capacity	1,200 gals.
Speed	65 mph.
Builder	EMD

(Courtesy of G. P. Barth.)

F7B

Penn Central, No. 3547, an F7B, assisting in pulling a train into Conway yards from the East. This is a vanishing locomotive, as are most B-units on American railroads. (Photo by author.)

Baltimore and Ohio No. 5420, an F7B, going in for refueling in New Castle, Pennsylvania. No. 5420 has the porthole in the side located differently than the Penn Central No. 3547 above. (Photo by author.)

F9A

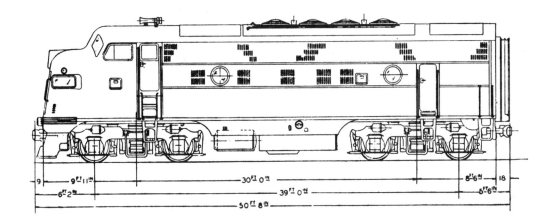

Horsepower	1,750
Engine	1 – 16 Cylinder V GM 567C
Main Generator	1 – EMD D12
Traction Motors	4 D47B1 or D37
Wheels	40″
Air Brakes	24RL
Wheel Base	
each truck	9′
truck centers	30′
Maximum Dimensions	
height	15′
between coupler pulling faces	50′–8″
Fuel Capacity	1,200 gals.
Speed	102 mph.
Builder	EMD

(Courtesy of
Electro-Motive Division of General Motors Corporation.)

F9B

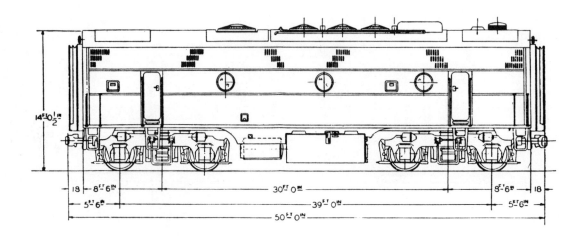

Horsepower	1,750
Engine	1 – 16 cylinder V
	GM 567C
Main Generator	1 – EMD D12
Traction Motors	4 – D74B1 or D37
Wheels	40″
Air Brakes	24RL
Wheel Base	
each truck	9′
truck centers	30′
Maximum Dimensions	
height	15′
between coupler pulling faces	50′
Fuel capacity	1,200 gals.
Speed	102 mph.
Builder	EMD

(Courtesy of
Electro-Motive Division of General Motors Corporation.)

F9A and F9B

1,750 hp. F9A and F9B units (with a second F9A in reverse as the third locomotive) of the Union Pacific pulling a freight train in the Columbia River Gorge, Oregon. The F9 locomotives were not nearly as widespread a locomotive, in terms of numbers of units produced, as were the F7s. (Courtesy of Union Pacific Railroad.)

FP7A

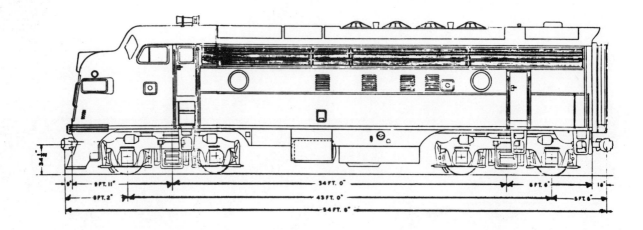

Horsepower	1,500
Engine	
1 – 16cylinder	GM 567B
Main Generator	1 Model D12–D14
Traction Motors	4 Model D27
Wheels	40″
Air Brakes	24RL
Wheel Base	
each truck	9′
truck centers	34′
Maximum Dimensions	
height	15′
between coupler pulling faces	54′–8″
Fuel capacity	1,200
Speed	102 mph.
Builder	EMD

(Courtesy of
Electro-Motive Division of General Motors Corporation.)

FP7A

Milwaukee No. 97-C, heavy-duty, 1,500 hp. FP7A unit. (Courtesy of the Milwaukee Road.)

The FP7A, Penn Central No. 4345, is a crossbreed locomotive. It was designed to be a freight locomotive and/or passenger locomotive. The FP7A is longer than the more widespread F7, sporting a steam generator in the rear of the carbody. It has the same horsepower, 1,500, as the F7. (Photo by author.)

FP7B

No. 4156, FP7B, is one of only two such units still operating on the Penn Central. Since it is a B-unit, it is only used as an auxillary locomotive. (Photo by author.)

FP9A

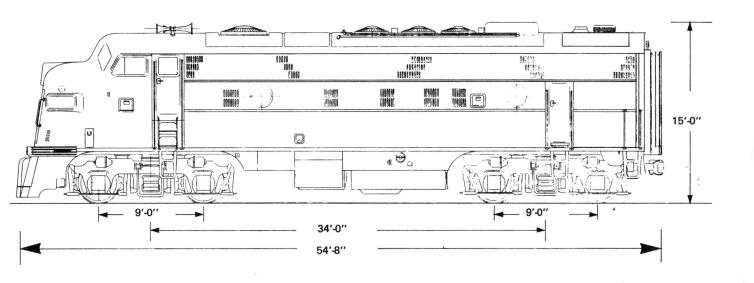

Horsepower	1,750
Engine	1 – 16 cylinder V GM 567C
Main Generator	1 – EMD D12
Traction Motors	4 D47B1
Wheels	40″
Air Brakes	24RL
Wheel Base	
each truck	9′
truck centers	34′
Maximum Dimensions	
height	15′
between coupler pulling faces	54′–8″
Fuel capacity	1,200 gals.
Speed	105 mph.
Builder	EMD

(Courtesy of
Electro-Motive Division of General Motors Corporation.)

FP9A

Canadian National No. 6526, an FP9A, backing up behind ALCO FPA4 in Toronto yards. (Photo by author.)

FP9B

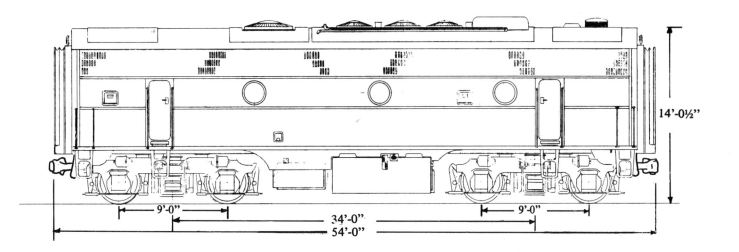

Horsepower	1,750
Engine	1 – 16 cylinder V
	GM 567C
Main Generator	1 – EMD D12
Traction Motors	4 D47B1
Wheels	40″
Air Brakes	24RL
Wheel Base	
each truck	9′
truck centers	34′
Maximum Dimensions	
height	15′
between coupler pulling faces	54′
Fuel capacity	1,200 gals.
Speed	105 mph.
Builder	EMD

(Courtesy of
Electro-Motive Division of General Motors Corporation.)

F45

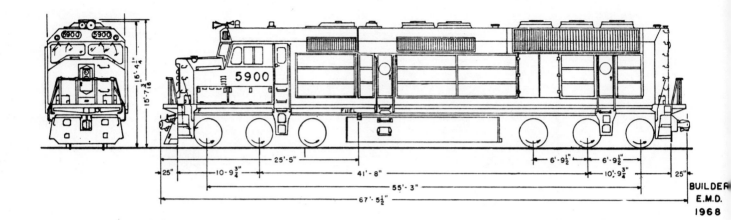

Horsepower	3,600
Engine	1 –20 cylinder V
	Model 645E3
Main Generator (Alternator)	EMD Model AR–10
Traction Motors	6 EMD Model D–77
Wheels	40″
Air Brakes	26L
Wheel Base	
each truck	13′–7″
truck centers	41′–8″
Maximum Dimensions	
height	15′–7–1/4″
between coupler pulling faces	67′–5–1/2″
Fuel capacity	3,200 gals.
Speed	83 mph.
Builder	EMD

(Courtesy of Atchison, Topeka, and Santa Fe Railroad.)

FA1

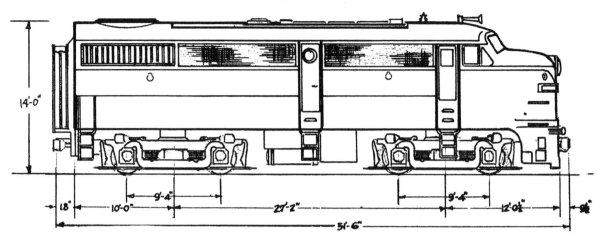

Horsepower	1,500
Engine	1 – 12 cylinder
Main Generator	1 GE Model GT 581
Traction Motors	4 GE Model 752
Wheels	40″
Air Brakes	24RL
Wheel Base	
each truck	9′–4″
truck centers	27′–2″
Maximum Dimensions	
height	14′–10″
between coupler pulling faces	51′–6″
Fuel capacity	1,000 Imperial gals.
Speed	75 mph.
Builder	ALCO

(Courtesy of Canadian National Railways.)

Union Pacific 1,500 hp. FA1, No. 1500A, ALCO freight locomotive. This locomotive no longer appears on the Union Pacific Locomotive Inventory List and is presumed to be deceased. (Courtesy of Union Pacific Railroad.)

FA2

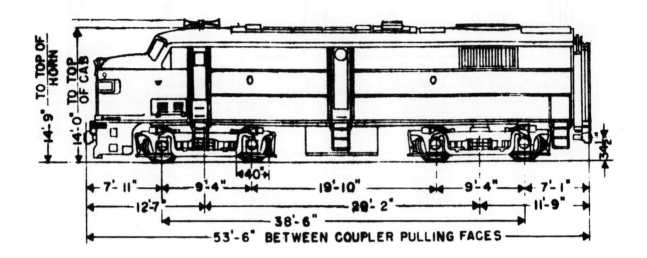

Horsepower	1,600
Engine	1 – 12 cylinder V
	ALCO 244
Main Generator	1 GE Model GT 581–A1
Traction Motors	4 GE Model 752–C1
Wheels	40″
Air Brakes	24RL
Wheel Base	
each truck	9′–4″
truck centers	29′–2″
Maximum Dimensions	
height	14′–9″
between coupler pulling faces	53′–6″
Fuel capacity	1,200 gals.
Speed	65 mph.
Builder	ALCO

(Courtesy of G. P. Barth.)

FA2

No. 302, FA2 of the Western Maryland Railroad. The FA2 was a 1,600 hp. freight locomotive. Very few last to this day, many having been scrapped. (Courtesy of Western Maryland Railroad.)

FB2

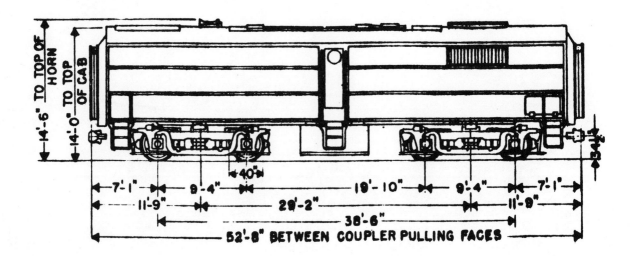

Horsepower	1,600
Engine	1 – 12 cylinder V ALCO Model 244
Main Generator	1 GE Model 581–A1 Direct Drive
Traction Motors	4 GE Model 752–C1
Wheels	40″
Air Brakes	24RL
Wheel Base	
each truck	9′–4″
truck centers	29′–2″
Maximum Dimensions	
height	14′–6–7/16″
between coupler pulling faces	52′–8″
Fuel capacity	1,200 gals.
Speed	65 mph.
Builder	ALCO

(Courtesy of G. P. Barth.)

FPA2

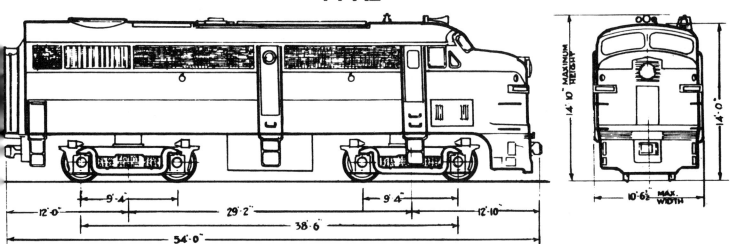

Horsepower	1,600
Engine	1 – 12 cylinder
Main Generator	1 GE Model GT 581
Traction Motors	4 GE Model 752
Wheels	40"
Air Brakes	24RL
Wheel Base	
each truck	9'–4"
truck centers	29'–2"
Maximum Dimensions	
height	14'–10"
between coupler pulling faces	54'
Fuel capacity	1,000 Imperial gals.
Speed	92 mph.
Builder	MLW

(Courtesy of Canadian National Railways.)

No. 6758 is an FPA2 built by the Montreal Locomotive Works and has a steam generator for use in passenger service. The basic design for this locomotive was after the ALCO FA series locomotives and built by MLW. This locomotive was built in 1955 and has 1,600 hp. No. 6758 is standing here behind the yardmaster's office in the Toronto yards of the Canadian National. The Canadian National owns three of these locomotives. (Photo by author.)

FPB2

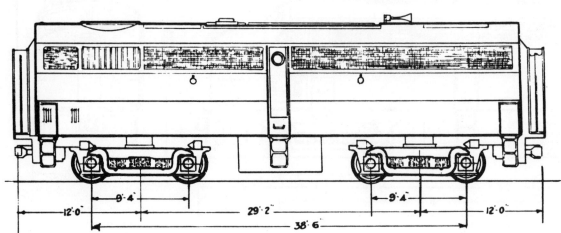

Horsepower	1,600
Engine	1 – 12 cylinder
Main Generator	1 GE Model GT 581
Traction Motors	4 GE Model 752
Wheels	40″
Air Brakes	24RL
Wheel Base	
each truck	9′–4″
truck centers	29′–2″
Maximum Dimensions	
height	14′–6–5/8″
between coupler pulling faces	53′–2″
Fuel capacity	1,000 Imperial gals.
Speed	92 mph.
Builder	MLW

(Courtesy of Canadian National Railways.)

Canadian Pacific FPB2, No. 4469, parked in the CP Rail yards in Toronto. It is a 1,600 hp. B-unit capable of being used in freight or passenger service. This unit has not received a new "CP Rail" paint job yet, so it shows here in the railroad's former color scheme. (Photo by author.)

FPA4

A pair of Canadian National FPA4s, 1,800 hp. units, in the CN Toronto yards. Nos. 6793 and 6787 are in regular freight service. (Photo by author.)

C418

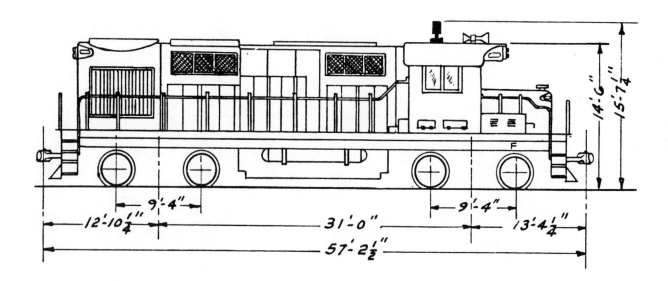

Horsepower	1,800
Engine	1 – 12 cylinder
Main Generator	1 GE Model 564 E1
Traction Motors	4 GE Model 752 C1
Wheels	40″
Air Brakes	26L
Wheel Base	
each truck	9′–4″
truck centers	31′
Maximum Dimensions	
height	15′–7-1/4″
between coupler pulling faces	57′–2-1/2″
Fuel capacity	1,500 gals.
Speed	70 mph.
Builder	ALCO

(Courtesy of Louisville and Nashville Railroad.)

MLW 420

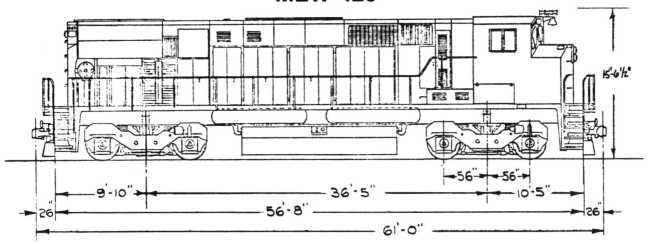

Horsepower	2,000
Engine	1 – 12 cylinder V
Main Generator (Alternator)	1 GTA 17PB1
Traction Motors	4 GE Model 752 PC6
Wheels	40″
Air Brakes	Westinghouse 26 LUM
Wheel Base	
each truck	9′–4″
truck centers	36′–5″
Maximum Dimensions	
height	15′–6–1/2″
between coupler pulling faces	61′
Fuel capacity	2,500 Imperial gals.
Speed	65 mph.
Builder	MLW

(Courtesy of Canadian National Railways.)

Canadian National No. 2500, MLW 420, built by the Montreal Locomotive Works. This snowy scene was in the Canadian National yards in Fort Erie, Ontario. (Photo by author.)

C420

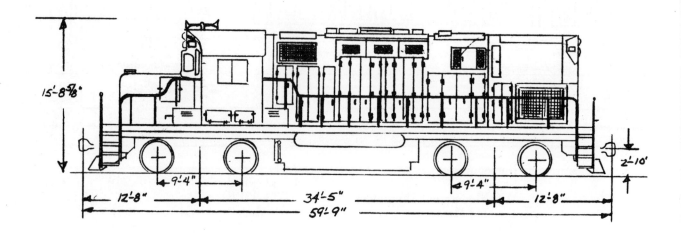

Horsepower	2,000
Engine	1 – 12 cylinder V
	Model 251
Main Generator	1 GE Model GT–581
Traction Motors	4 GE Model 752
Wheels	40"
Air Brakes	26L
Wheel Base	
each truck	9'–4"
truck centers	34'–5"
Maximum Dimensions	
height	15'–8–5/8"
between coupler pulling faces	60'–3"
Fuel capacity	2,000 gals.
Speed	86 mph.
Builder	ALCO

(Courtesy of E. L. Robinson.)

C420

Lehigh Valley No. 411, C420, leading a freight east-bound from Buffalo. The C420 is a 2,000 hp. road locomotive built by ALCO. No. 410 following is also a C420, turned so that the back of the locomotive is going forward. (Photo by author.)

C424

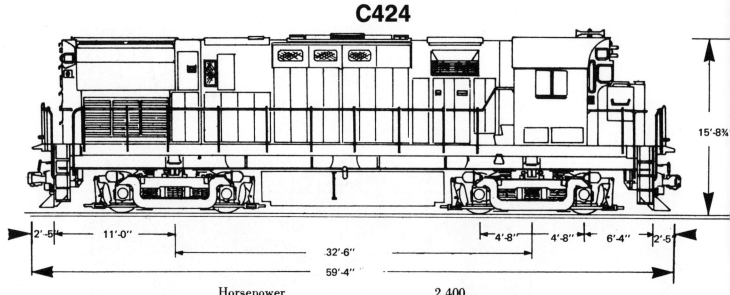

2'-5" 11'-0" 32'-6" 4'-8" 4'-8" 6'-4" 2'-5" 59'-4" 15'-8¾"

Horsepower	2,400
Engine	1 – 16 cylinder V Model 251
Main Generator	1 GE Model GT 581
Traction Motors	4 GE Model 752
Wheels	40"
Air Brakes	26L
Wheel Base	
each truck	9'–4"
truck centers	32'–6"
Maximum Dimensions	
height	15'–8–5/8"
between coupler pulling faces	59'–4"
Fuel capacity	2,000 gals.
Speed	86 mph.
Builder	ALCO

(Courtesy of S. S. Lingenfelter.)

Canadian Pacific ALCO C424, No. 4201, a 2,400 hp. road locomotive parked ahead of CP Rail No. 5024, a GP35, in the CP Rail Toronto yards. (Photo by author.)

C425

No. 2426, an ALCO C425, coming into Conway yards, north of Pittsburgh, Pennsylvania, on the Penn Central. (Photo by author.)

Horsepower	2,500
Engine	1 – 16 cylinder V
	Model 251
Main Generator	1 GE Model GT–598
Traction Motors	4 GE Model 752
Wheels	40″
Air Brakes	26L
Wheel Base	
each truck	9′–4″
truck centers	32′–6″
Maximum Dimensions	
height	15′–8–5/8″
between coupler pulling faces	59′–4″
Fuel capacity	2,000 gals.
Speed	86 mph.
Builder	ALCO

(Courtesy of S. S. Lingenfelter.)

C430

Penn Central No. 2056, C430, in Conway yards. A 3,000 hp. locomotive, it is a road locomotive. (Photo by author.)

Horsepower	3,000
Engine	1 – 16 cylinder V Model 251
Main Generator (Alternator)	1 GE Model GT–A9A
Traction Motors	4 GE Model 752
Wheels	40″
Air Brakes	26L
Wheel Base	
each truck	9′–4″
truck centers	36′–9″
Maximum Dimensions	
height	15′–7–9/16″
between coupler pulling faces	63′–1″
Fuel capacity	3,000 gals.
Speed	78 mph.
Builder	ALCO

(Courtesy of S. S. Lingenfelter.)

C628

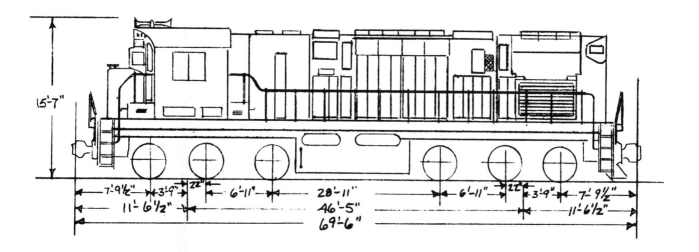

Horsepower	2,750
Engine	1 – 16 cylinder V Model 251
Main Generator	1 GE Model GT–586
Traction Motors	6 GE Model 752
Wheels	40″
Air Brakes	26L
Wheel Base	
each truck	12′–6″
truck centers	46′–5″
Maximum Dimensions	
height	15′–7″
between coupler pulling faces	69′–6″
Fuel capacity	4,000 gals.
Speed	80 mph.
Builder	ALCO

(Courtesy of E. L. Robinson.)

C628

Penn Central C628, No. 6305, leaving the turntable at Conway yards. The Penn Central owns fifteen of these 2,750 hp. locomotives. (Photo by author.)

Three Louisville and Nashville (Family Lines System) ALCO C628s. The total horsepower pulling this train in the three locomotives is 8,250. (Courtesy of Louisville and Nashville Railroad.)

MLW 630

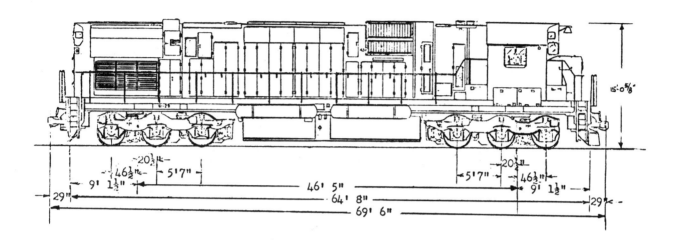

Horsepower	3,000
Engine	1 – 16 cylinder
Main Generator (Alternator)	1 GE Model GTA 9E2
Traction Motors	6 GE Model 752 PC6
Wheels	40″
Air Brakes	Westinghouse 26L
Wheel Base	
each truck	11′–2″
truck centers	43′
Maximum Dimensions	
height	15′–0–5/8″
between coupler pulling faces	69′–6″
Fuel capacity	3,200 Imperial gals.
Speed	75 mph.
Builder	MLW

(Courtesy of Canadian National Railways.)

MLW 630

No. 4730, CP Rail MLW 630, standing in Toronto
yards. It is a 3,000 hp. freight locomotive. (Photo by
author.)

C630

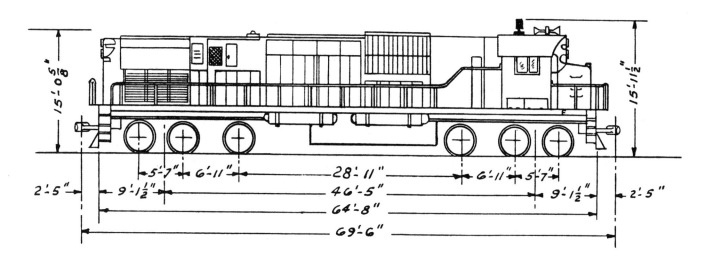

Horsepower	3,000
Engine	1 – 16 cylinder V Model 251
Main Generator	1 GE Model GTA9A
Traction Motors	6 GE Model 752
Wheels	40″
Air Brakes	26L
Wheel Base	
each truck	12′–6″
truck centers	46′–5″
Maximum Dimensions	
height	15′–7″
between coupler pulling faces	69′–6″
Fuel capacity	4,000 gals.
Speed	80 mph.
Builder	ALCO

(Courtesy of Louisville and Nashville Railroad.)

C630

Louisville and Nashville Nos. 1425, 1426, and one other C630 pull a freight train through a grade crossing. There is a total of 9,000 horsepower pulling this train. (Courtesy of Louisville and Nashville Railroad.)

Penn Central No. 6325, a C630, pulling a train of empty hopper cars out of Conway yards. (Photo by author.)

MLW 636

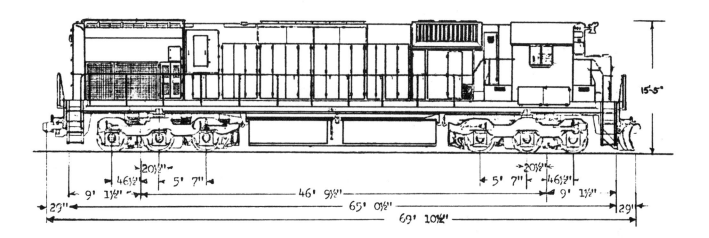

Horsepower	3,600
Engine	1 – 16 cylinder
Main Generator	1 CGE Model 5GT A11 BD2
Traction Motors	6 CGE Model 752 PC6
Wheels	40″
Air Brakes	Westinghouse 26 LUM
Wheel Base	
each truck	11′–2″
truck centers	43′–4–1/2″
Maximum Dimensions	
height	15′–5″
between coupler pulling faces	69′–10–1/2″
Fuel capacity	3,400 Imperial gals.
Speed	75 mph.
Builder	MLW

(Courtesy of Canadian National Railways.)

C636

Penn Central No. 6342, ALCO C636, helping to pull a train westbound from Pittsburgh, Pennsylvania. It is a heavy, six-axle, 3,600 np. locomotive. This locomotive has high-adhesion trucks to help prevent wheel slippage. (Photo by author.)

U18B

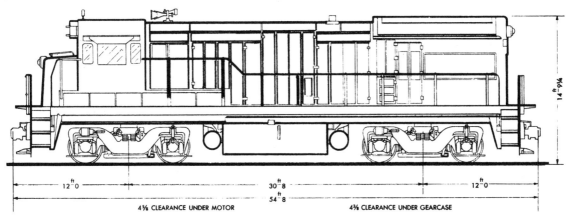

4⅜ CLEARANCE UNDER MOTOR   4⅜ CLEARANCE UNDER GEARCASE

Horsepower	1,800
Engine	1 – GE Model FDL8
Main Generator	1 GTA11
Traction Motors	4 GE Model 752
Wheels	40″
Air Brakes	26L
Wheel Base	
each truck	9′–0″
truck centers	30′–8″
Maximum Dimensions	
height	14′–9–1/4″
between coupler pulling faces	54′–8″
Fuel capacity	1,200 gals.
Speed	70 mph.
Builder	GE (General Electric Transportation Systems Division.)

(Courtesy of General Electric, Transportation Systems Division.)

Seaboard U18B, No. 302, of the Family Lines System. (Courtesy of the Family Lines System.)

U23B

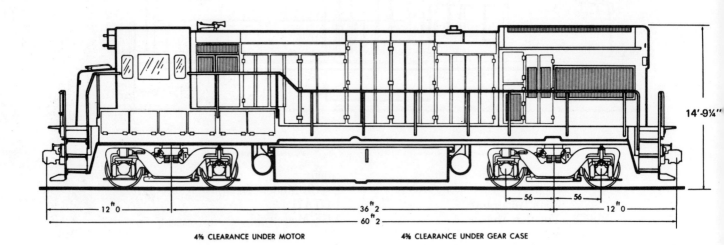

4% CLEARANCE UNDER MOTOR   4% CLEARANCE UNDER GEAR CASE

Horsepower	2,250
Engine	1 – GE Model FDL12
Main Generator	1 GTA11
Traction Motors	4 GE Model 752
Wheels	40″
Air Brakes	26L
Wheel Base	
each truck	9′–0″
truck centers	36′–2″
Maximum Dimensions	
height	14′–9–1/4″
between coupler pulling faces	60′–)″
Fuel capacity	1,700
Speed	70 mph.
Builder	GE

(Courtesy of General Electric, Transportation Systems Division.)

U23B

No. 604, Monon U23B, (now part of Louisville and Nashville, which is in turn part of the Family Lines System), in the Delaware and Hudson Colonie yards. (Courtesy of George W. Hockaday; Delaware and Hudson Railroad.)

U23B, No. 2719, four-axle smaller cousin of the General Electric U23C. It also has 2,250 hp. and is a relatively new addition to the Penn Central. (Photo by author.)

U23C

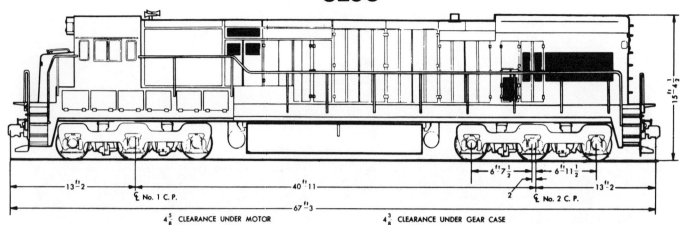

4⅝ CLEARANCE UNDER MOTOR   4⅜ CLEARANCE UNDER GEAR CASE

Horsepower	2,250
Engine	1 – GE Model FDL
Main Generator	1 GTA 586
Traction Motors	6 GE Model 752
Wheels	40″
Air Brakes	26L
Wheel Base	
each truck	13′–9″
truck centers	40′–11″
Maximum Dimensions	
height	15′–4–1/2″
between coupler pulling faces	67′–3″
Fuel capacity	3,000 gals.
Speed	70 mph.
Builder	GE

(Courtesy of General Electric, Transportation Systems Division.)

Penn Central No. 6703, U23C, a 2,250 hp. locomotive used as a hump engine at Frontier yard in Buffalo. No. 6703 works with a GP9B unit (not shown) to push trains of cars over the hump into the classification yard. (Photo by author.)

U25B

MODEL-U25B

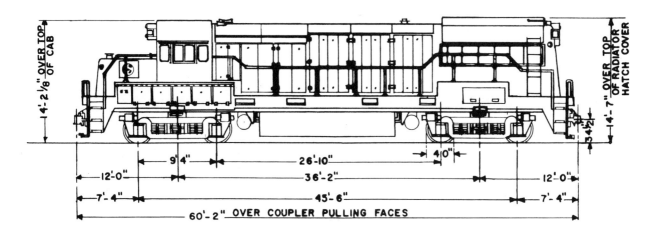

Horsepower	2,500	
Engine	1–16 cylinder	
	GE Model FDL–16	
Main Generator	1 GE Model GT598 C3	
Traction Motors	4 GE Model 752	
Wheels	40″	
Air Brakes	26L	
Wheel Base		
each truck	9′–4″	
truck centers	36′–2″	
locomotive	45′–6″	
Maximum Dimensions		
height	14′–7″	
between coupler pulling faces	60′–2′	
Fuel capacity	1,700 gals.	
Speed	85 mph.	
Builder	GEX	

(Courtesy of S. S. Lingenfelter.)

U25B

Erie-Lackawanna No. 2502, U25B, hauling freight between Niagara Falls, New York, and Buffalo, New York. It is seen here in North Tonawanda, New York. (Photo by author.)

Union Pacific No. 628, U25B, with others pulling eastbound freight in Echo Canyon, Utah. These are examples of the high-hood model U25B. (Courtesy of Union Pacific Railroad.)

U25C

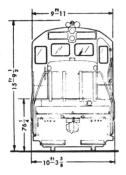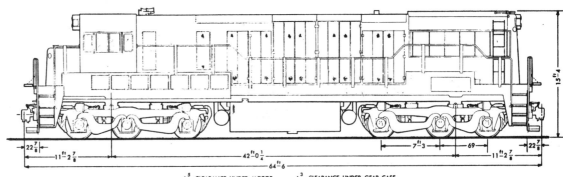

Horsepower	2,500
Engine	1 – Model 7FDL–16
Main Generator	1 GE Model GT–586
Traction Motors	6 GE Model 752
Wheels	40″
Air Brakes	26L
Wheel Base	
each truck	13′
truck centers	42′
Maximum Dimensions	
height	15′–4″
between coupler pulling faces	64′–6″
Fuel capacity	2,900 gals.
Speed	70 mph.
Builder	GE

(Courtesy of General Electric, Transportation Systems Division.)

Penn Central No. 6505, U25C, pulling a freight train into Conway yards, near Freedom, Pennsylvania. The U25C was in production by General Electric from 1963 to 1965. A total of ninety-seven units have been built thus far. The Penn Central owns twenty of them. (Photo by author.)

207

U28B

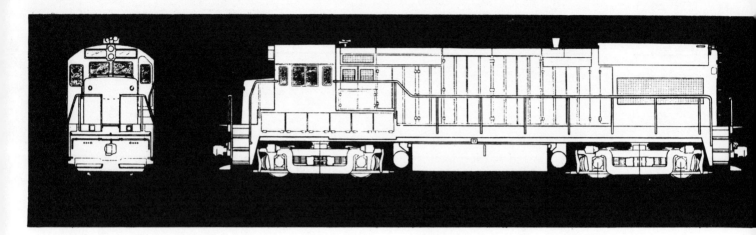

Horsepower	2,800
Engine	1 – 16 cylinder V Model 7 FDL–16
Main Generator	1 GE Model GT 598
Traction Motors	4 GE Model 752
Wheels	40-6P
Air Brakes	26L
Wheel Base	
each truck	9'–4"
truck centers	36'
Maximum Dimensions	
height	14'–7–1/2"
between coupler pulling faces	60'–2"
Fuel capacity	1,700 gals.
Speed	85 mph.
Builder	GE

(Courtesy of General Electric, Transportation Systems Division.)

U28B

Pittsburgh and Lake Erie Railroad No. 2806, U28B, moving fast across the Ohio River Bridge, through Beaver, Pennsylvania, and westward. (Photo by author.)

Milwaukee Road U28B, No. 397, fitted with a snowplow. (Courtesy of the Milwaukee Road.)

U28C

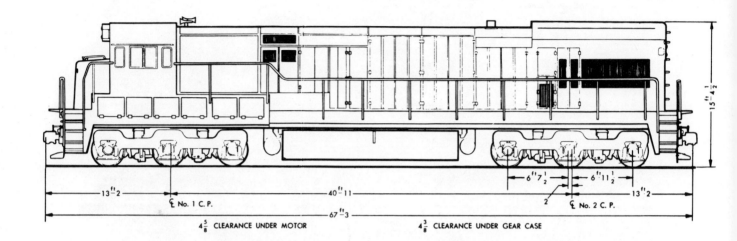

Horsepower	2,800
Engine	1 – Model 7FDL–12
Main Oenerator	1 GE Model 67 A11
Traction Motors	6 GE Model 752
Wheels	40″
Air Brakes	26L
Wheel Base	
each truck	13′–9″
truck centers	40′–11″
Maximum Dimensions	
height	15′–4–1/2″
between coupler pulling faces	67′–3″
Fuel capacity	3,000/4,000 gals.
Speed	70 mph.
Builder	GE

(Courtesy of General Electric, Transportation Systems Division.)

U28C

Union Pacific No. 2804, U28C, standing at Council Bluffs. This is a six-axle, 2,800, hp., General Electric product. There were eighty-eight of these built in 1965 and 1966. The Union Pacific owns ten of them. (Courtesy of Union Pacific Railroad.)

Penn Central No. 6532, U28C, former Pennsylvania locomotive following an SD45 into Conway yards. Fifteen of the U28Cs work for the Penn Central. (Photo by author.)

U30B

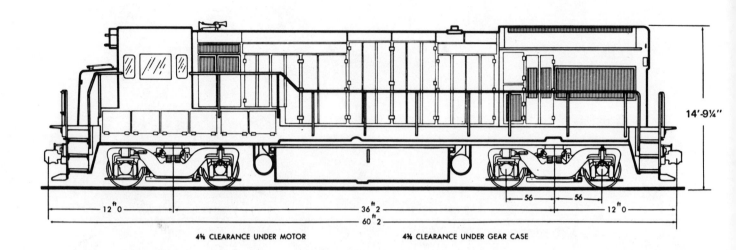

4⅝ CLEARANCE UNDER MOTOR   4⅝ CLEARANCE UNDER GEAR CASE

Horsepower	3,000
Engine	1 – GE Model FDL16
Main Generator	1 GTA11
Traction Motors	4 GE Model 752
Wheels	40"
Air Brakes	26L
Wheel Base	
each truck	9'–4"
truck centers	36'–2"
Maximum Dimensions	
height	14'–9–1/4"
between coupler pulling faces	60'–2"
Fuel capacity	1,700 gals.
Speed	75 mph.
Builder	GE

(Courtesy of General Electric, Transportation Systems Division.)

U30B

**Penn Central U30B, No. 2886, parked on a siding in
Niagara Falls during the winter.** (Photo by author.)

Norfolk and Western No. 8511, U30B. (Courtesy of
Norfolk and Western Railroad.)

U30C

Horsepower   3,000
Engine   1 – GE Model FDL16
Main Generator   1 GE Model GTA–11
Traction Motors   6 GE Model 752
Wheels   40″
Air Brakes   26L
Wheel Base
    each truck   13′–9″
    truck centers   40′–11″
Maximum Dimensions
    height   15′–4–1/2″
    between coupler pulling faces   67′–3″
Fuel capacity   3,000/4,000 gals.
Speed   70 mph.
Builder   GE

(Courtesy of General Electric, Transportation Systems Division.)

Delaware and Hudson U30C, No. 704, followed by U30C, No. 706, across a grade crossing. The Delaware and Hudson owns twelve other U30Cs numbered 701 through 712. (Courtesy of George W. Hockaday; Delaware and Hudson Railroad.)

U33B

14'-9¼"

12 ft 0   36 ft 2   56   56   12 ft 0
                 60 ft 2

4¾ CLEARANCE UNDER MOTOR   4¾ CLEARANCE UNDER GEAR CASE

Horsepower	3,300
Engine	1 – GE Model FDL
Main Generator	1 GTA–11
Traction Motors	4 GE Model 752
Wheels	40"
Air Brakes	26L
Wheel Base	
each truck	9'–4"
truck centers	36'–2"
Maximum Dimensions	
height	14'–9–1/4"
between coupler pulling faces	60'–2"
Fuel capacity	1,700 gals.
Speed	75 mph.
Builder	GE

(Courtesy of General Electric, Transportation Systems Division.)

A pair of U33Bs, Seaboard Nos. 1721 and 1722, coupled to each other back to back. (Courtesy of the Seaboard Coast Line.)

U33C

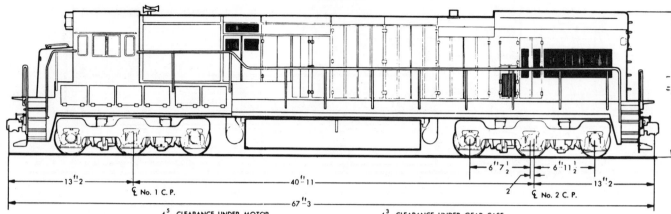

4 5/8″ CLEARANCE UNDER MOTOR   4 3/8″ CLEARANCE UNDER GEAR CASE

Horsepower	3,300
Engine	1 – GE Model FDL 16
Main Generator	1 GTA11
Traction Motors	6 GE Model 752
Wheels	40″
Air Brakes	26L
Wheel Base	
each truck	13′—9″
truck centers	40′–11″
Maximum Dimensions	
height	15′–4–1/2″
between coupler pulling faces	67′–3″
Fuel capacity	3,000/4,000 gals.
Speed	70 mph.
Builder	GE

(Courtesy of General Electric, Transportation Systems Division.)

Six-axle U33C, of the Delaware and Hudson Railroad, No. 752, seen at the Colonie Shop. (Courtesy of George W. Hockaday; Delaware and Hudson Railroad.)

U36B

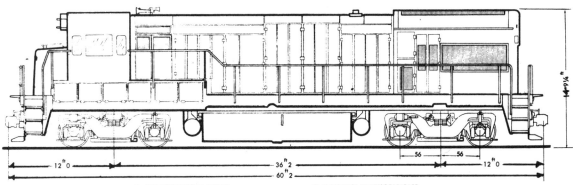

4% CLEARANCE UNDER MOTOR   4% CLEARANCE UNDER GEAR CASE

Horsepower	3,600
Engine	1 – GE Model FDL16
Main Generator	11 GTA11
Traction Motors	4 GE Model 752
Wheels	40"
Air Brakes	26L
Wheel Base	
each truck	9'–4"
truck centers	36'–2"
Maximum Dimensions	
height	14'–9–1/4"
between coupler pulling faces	60'–2"
Fuel capacity	1,700 gals.
Speed	75 mph.
Builder	GE

(Courtesy of General Electric, Transportation Systems Division.)

No. 1766, U36B, of the Seaboard Coast Line, the smaller four-axle, 3,600 hp. cousin of the U36C, parked at the station platform. (Courtesy of Seaboard Coast Line/Family Lines System.)

U36C

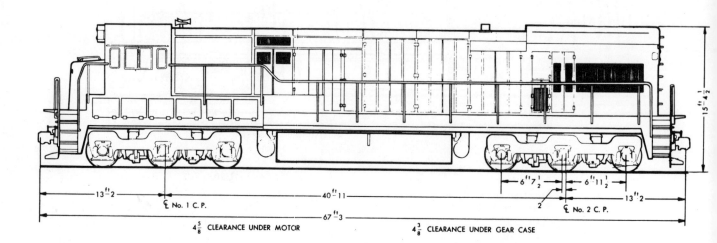

Horsepower	3,600
Engine	1 – GE Model FDL16
Main Generator	1 GE Model GTA11
Traction Motors	6 GE Model 752
Wheels	40″
Air Brakes	26L
Wheel Base	
each truck	13′–9″
truck centers	40′–11″
Maximum Dimensions	
height	15′–4–1/2″
between coupler pulling faces	67′–3″
Fuel capacity	3,000/4,000 gals.
Speed	70 mph.
Builder	GE

(Courtesy of General Electric, Transportation Systems Division.)

U36C

Santa Fe U36C, a 3,600 hp., six-axle, road-freight locomotive built by General Electric. The Santa Fe owns thirty-six U36Cs. (Courtesy of Atchison, Topeka, and Santa Fe Railroad.)

7

MONSTER LOCOMOTIVES

Grouped by manufacturer in the approximate
order of their appearance on American railroads.

U50

Union Pacific No. 32, 5,000 hp. U50, built by General Electric. (Courtesy of Union Pacific Railroad.)

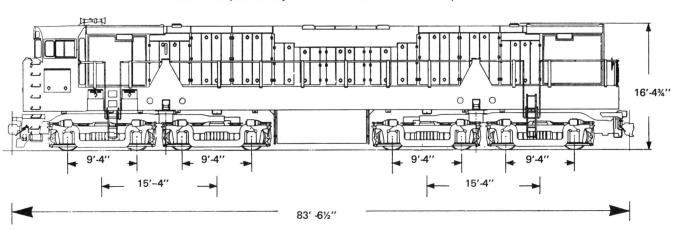

Horsepower	5,000
Engine	2—16 cylinder V FDL-16
Main Generator	2 GE GT598
Traction Motors	8 GE Model 752
Wheels	40″
Air Brakes	26L
Wheel Base	
each truck	9′—4″
truck centers	2—15′—4″ each
Maximum Dimensions	
height	16′—4¾″
between coupler pulling faces	83′—6½″
Fuel Capacity	5,800 gals.
Speed	80 mph.
Builder	General Electric

(Courtesy of General Electric Company
Transportation Systems Division.)

(Reprinted with permission of
Simmons-Boardman Publishing Corporation.)

U50C

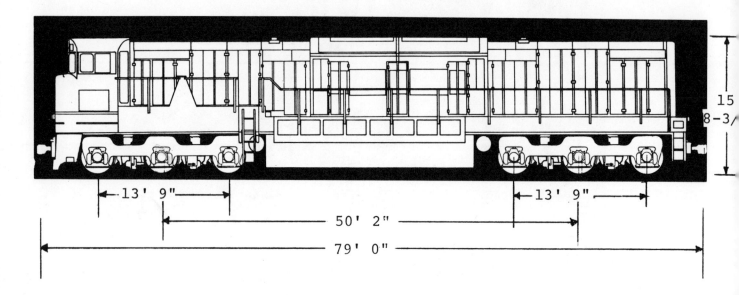

Horsepower	5,000
Engine	2 – 12 cylinder V
	Model FDL–12
Main Generator (Alternator)	2 GE Model GTA–11
Traction Motors	6 GE Model 752
Wheels	40″
Air Brakes	26L
Wheel Base	
each truck	13′–7″
truck centers	50′–2″
Maximum Dimensions	
height	15′–8–3/4″
between coupler pulling faces	79′–0″
Fuel capacity	5,000 gals.
Speed	75 mph.
Builder	GE

(Courtesy of General Electric, TranspToration Systems Division.)

U50C

The Union Pacific 5,000 hp., U50C, No. 5002, a true monster locomotive. This is not a commonly seen locomotive. (Courtesy of Union Pacific Railroad.)

DD35A

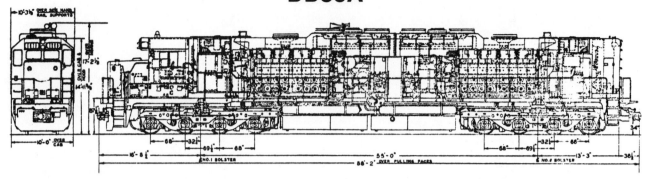

Horsepower	5,000
Engine	2 – 2,500 horsepower each
Main Generator	2 Model D32
Traction Motors	8 GE Model 752 E20A
Wheels	40″
Air Brakes	26L
Wheel Base	
each truck	17′–1–1/4″
truck centers	55′
Maximum Dimensions	
height	17′–2–1/8″
between coupler pulling faces	88′–2″
Fuel capacity	5,200 gals.
Speed	90 mph.
Builder	EMD

(Courtesy of Union Pacific Railroad.)

Union Pacific DD35A, 5,000 hp., eight-axle locomotive No. 71. The DD35 is the equivalent of two GP35 power systems put together on a long frame. It was built by General Motors (EMD). (Courtesy of Union Pacific Railroad.)

DD35B

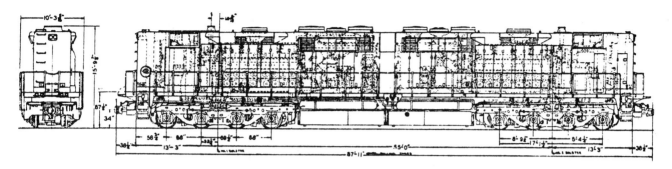

Horsepower	5,000
Engine	2 – 2,500 horsepower each
Main Generator	2 Model D32
Traction Motors	8 GE Model 752 E20A
Wheels	40″
Air Brakes	26L
Wheel Base	
each truck	17′–1–1/4″
truck centers	55′
Maximum Dimensions	
height	15′–9–7/8″
between coupler pulling faces	87′–11″
Fuel capacity	5,200 gals.
Speed	71 mph.
Builder	EMD

(Courtesy of Union Pacific Railroad.)

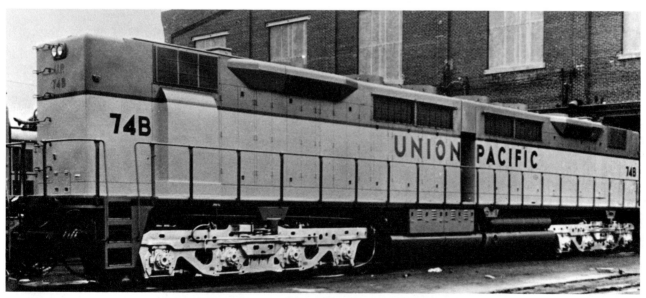

Union Pacific, No. 74B, DD35B unit. This eight-axle locomotive has no cab and is used to serve as an auxillary locomotive. It is as if two GP35s were put together on one frame. (Courtesy of Union Pacific Railroad.)

DD40

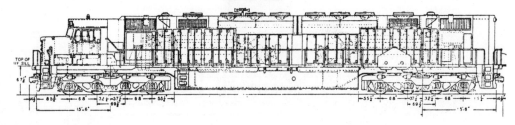

Horsepower	6,600
Engine	2 – 3,300 horsepower each
	16 cylinder
Main Generator (Alternator)	2 Model AR12
Traction Motors	8 Model D77X
Wheels	40"
Air Brakes	26L
Wheel Base	
each truck	17'–1–1/2"
truck centers	65'
Maximum Dimensions	
height	17'–3–13/16"
between coupler pulling faces	98'–5"
Fuel capacity	6,200 gals.
Speed	90 mph.
Builder	EMD

(Courtesy of Union Pacific Railroad.)

No. 6900, DD40, 6,600 hp. Centennial Locomotive of the Union Pacific Railroad. The Union Pacific traditionally seeks tremendous horsepower in road locomotives and this eight-axle monster is a good example of that tradition. This locomotive has 600 more horsepower than two 3,000 hp., GP40s hooked together. (Courtesy of Union Pacific Railroad.)

C855A

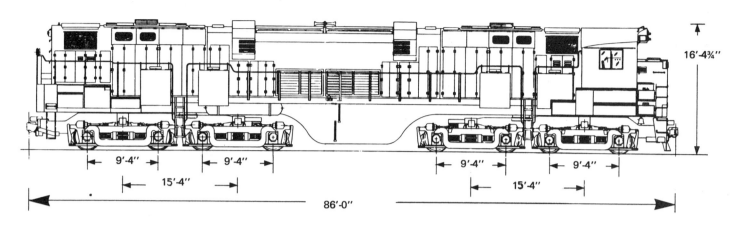

Horsepower	5,500	
Engine	2 — 2,750 horsepower each	
Main Generator	2 GE Model 598D1	
Traction Motors	8 ALCO Type Doughnut	
Wheels	40"	
Air Brakes	26L	
Wheel Base		
each truck	9'–4"	
truck centers	2—15'—4" each	
Maximum Dimensions		
height	16'–4–3/4"	
between coupler pulling faces	86'	
Fuel capacity	6,000 gals.	
Speed	70 mph.	
Builder	ALCO	

(Courtesy of Union Pacific Railroad.)

(Reprinted with permission of
Simmons-Boardman Publishing Corporation.)

C855A and C855B

Union Pacific Nos. 61 and 60B, ALCO C855A- &
B-units, 5,500 hp. each, with another C855A at the
end (in reverse). This, as with other high-
horsepower locomotives, are most widely used in
the Western United States where there are great
distances to cover in a hurry. (Courtesy of Union
Pacific Railroad.)

8
MAPS

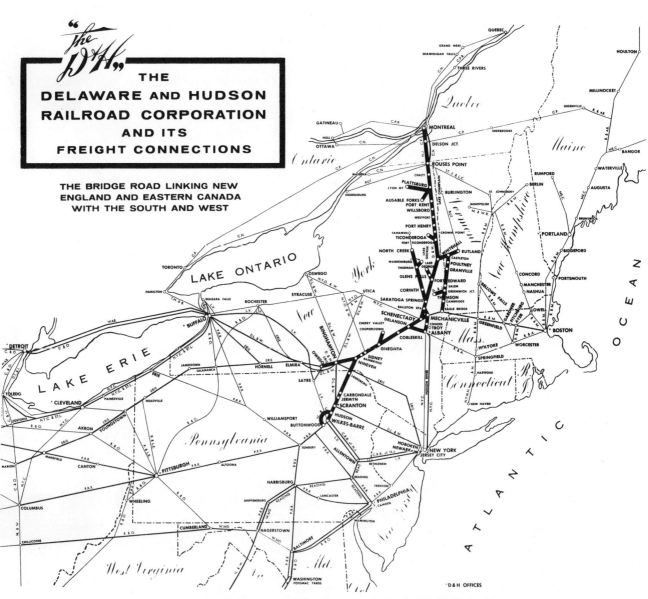

(Courtesy of the Delaware and Hudson Railroad
Corporation.)

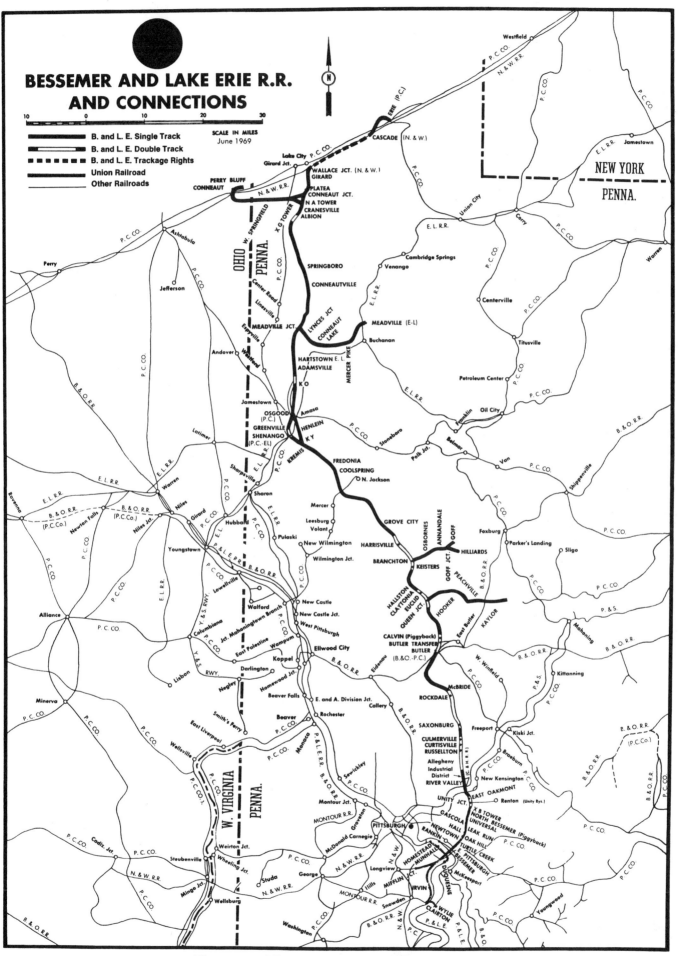

BESSEMER AND LAKE ERIE R.R. AND CONNECTIONS

B. and L. E. Single Track
B. and L. E. Double Track
B. and L. E. Trackage Rights
Union Railroad
Other Railroads

SCALE IN MILES
June 1969

(Courtesy of Bessemer and Lake Erie Railroad.)

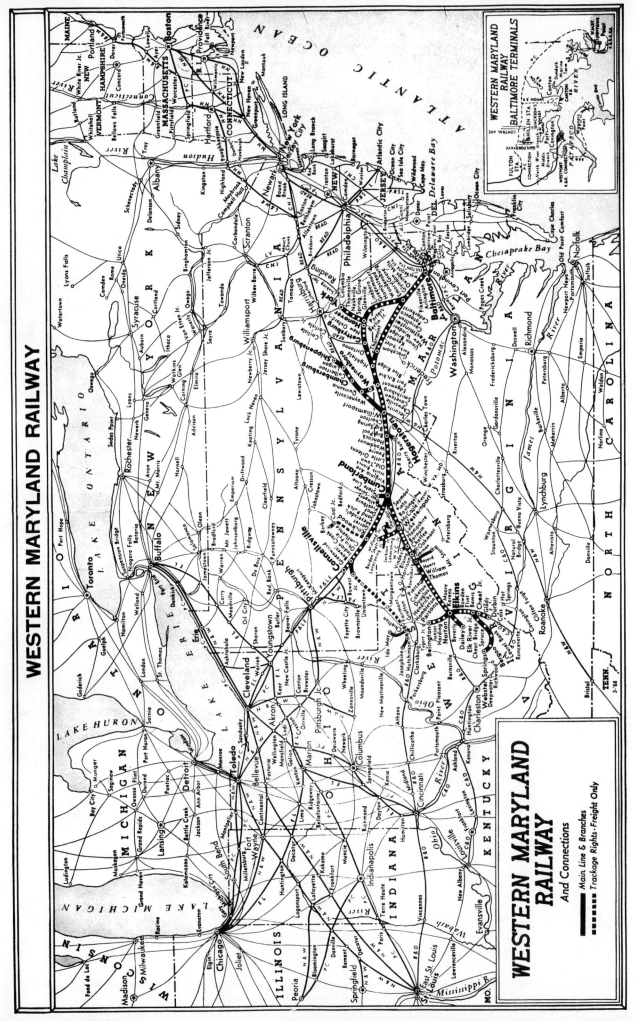

WESTERN MARYLAND RAILWAY

WESTERN MARYLAND RAILWAY
And Connections

Main Line & Branches
Trackage Rights-Freight Only

(Courtesy of Western Maryland Railway.)

THE FAMILY LINES.

SEABOARD COAST LINE RAILROAD

LOUISVILLE AND NASHVILLE RAILROAD

SUBSIDIARY RAILROADS

AFFILIATED RAILROADS

(Courtesy of the Family Lines System.)

233

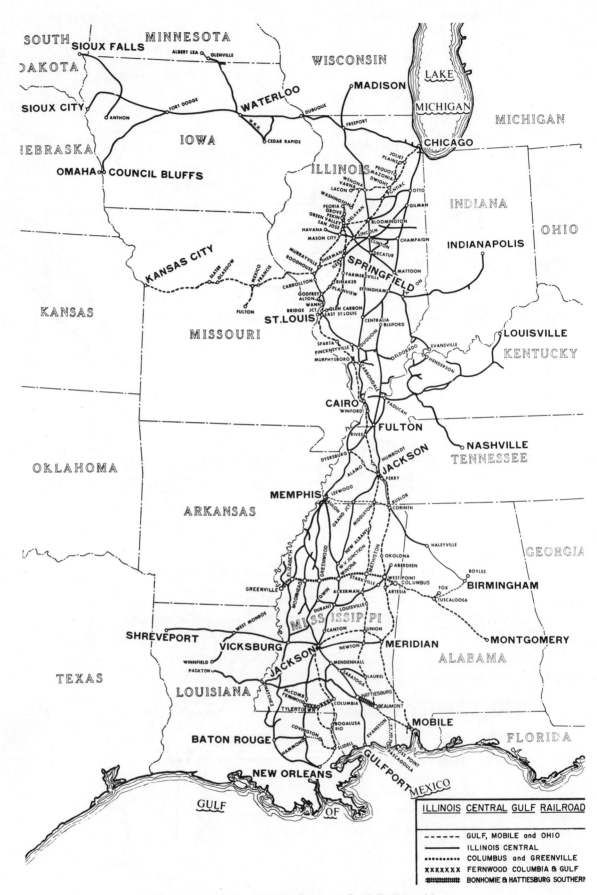

(Courtesy of the Illinois Central Gulf Railroad.)

234

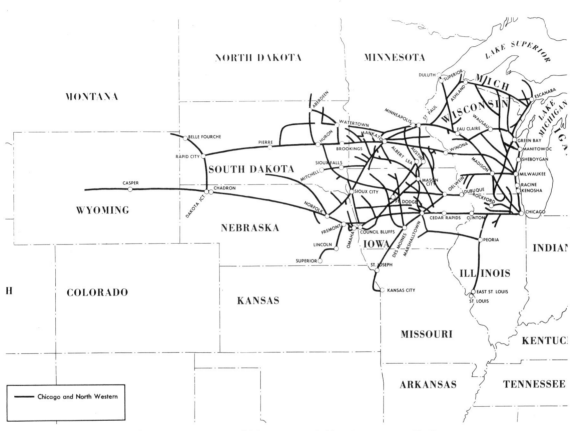

(Courtesy of the Chicago and Northwestern Railroad.)

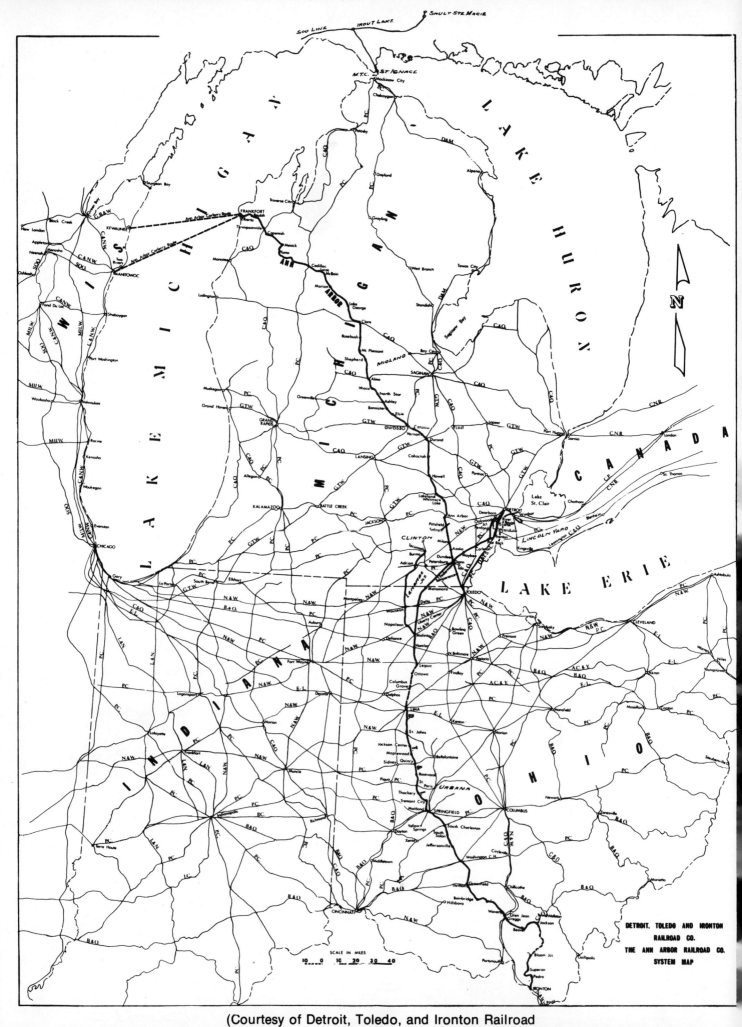

(Courtesy of Detroit, Toledo, and Ironton Railroad
Company.)

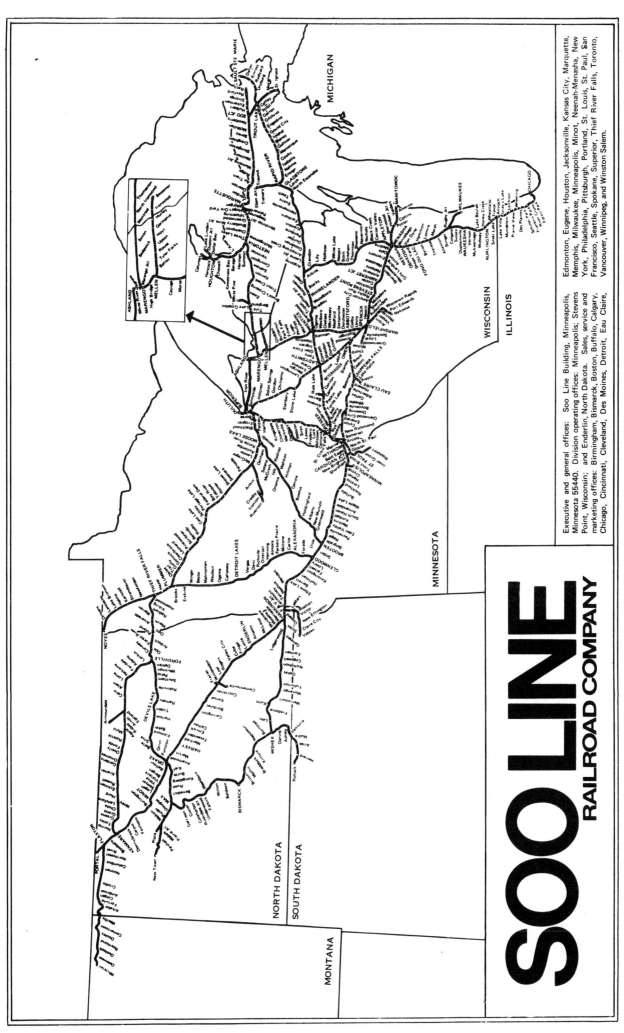

SOO LINE
RAILROAD COMPANY

Executive and general offices: Soo Line Building, Minneapolis, Minnesota 55440. Division operating offices: Minneapolis; Stevens Point, Wisconsin; and Enderlin, North Dakota. Sales, service and marketing offices: Birmingham, Bismarck, Boston, Buffalo, Calgary, Chicago, Cincinnati, Cleveland, Des Moines, Detroit, Eau Claire,

Edmonton, Eugene, Houston, Jacksonville, Kansas City, Marquette, Memphis, Milwaukee, Minneapolis, Minot, Neenah-Menasha, New York, Philadelphia, Pittsburgh, Portland, St. Louis, St. Paul, San Francisco, Seattle, Spokane, Superior, Thief River Falls, Toronto, Vancouver, Winnipeg, and Winston Salem.

(Courtesy of Soo Line Railroad Company.)

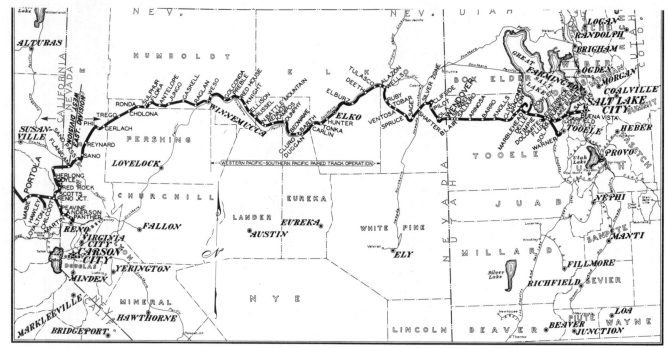

Map of the Eastern Division of the Western Pacific Railroad. (Courtesy of the Western Pacific Railroad.)

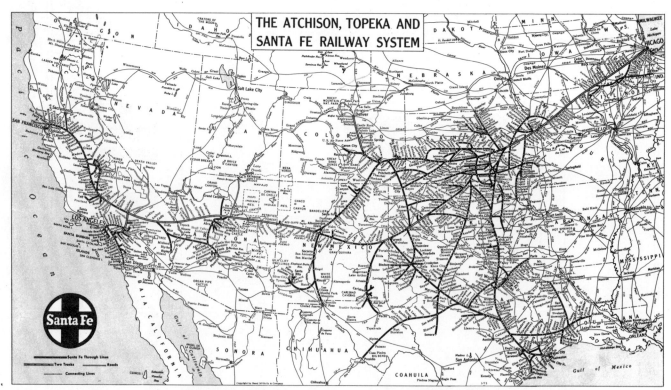

(Courtesy of the Atchison, Topeka, and Santa Fe Railroad. Reprinted with permission of Rand McNally.)

9
EPILOGUE

The outlook of locomotives is summed up by *Railroads of America*:

It is apparent that the need for rail services will continue to grow with the ever-expanding economy of the nation. And the railroads are busily gearing up to meet the tremendous challenges of the future. The United States Census Bureau anticipates a population increase from the 200 million plus of today to as many as 300 million by the year 2000. Approximately 75% of this booming population will be clustered around metropolitan areas.

What will this mean in terms of transportation demands? An idea can be gleaned from the prediction of the Department of Agriculture that annual crop production by 1980 will be one-and-a-third times the present level. All the farm products needed to feed the nation must be transported from farm to market or to processing plants and thence to market.

Another clue can be found in the predictions of the National Coal Policy Conference that 500 million tons of coal will be needed for electric-power generation in 1980. That is more than double the present consumption.

Broadly speaking, a "second America" will have to be built between now and the year 2000 to accommodate the expanded population. This means that almost unbelievable loads will have to be moved across the country and within our cities. The railroads — traditional workhorse of the nation's transportation industry — will have a tremendous role to play.

They may well play it as dynamic partners in full-fledged transportation companies, capable of providing complete transportation services to customers, regardless of the methods required. The development of commonly owned, intermodal companies of this type is presently inhibited by law. But, as transportation load-demands continue to grow and the inadequacy of past approaches to transport problems becomes more apparent, national policy changes are inevitable.

Such changes have long been encouraged by the railroad industry as essential to national progress. America is going to need all the good transportation it can get and the best is yet to come from her railroads.[8]

The future of railroading will look a lot different from the present and certainly from the past. "Metroliners and Turbotrains now plying the rails in the Washinton-New York-Boston corridor also represent a new breed of the familiar old Iron Horse."[9]

The fastest trains on the Penn Central's Metroliner

trains run between Washington and New York. At times these trains reach speeds of 120 miles per hour. The fastest of these trains covers the entire 226-mile distance in 2½ hours, an average speed of more than 90 miles per hour.

Among conventional trains, the fastest speed in the United States is found on the Burlington Northern Twin Cities *Zephyr*, which covers 45.25 miles in 32 minutes, an average speed of 84.8 miles per hour.

As such, these trains are dramatic symbols of progress. But they are only the "tip of the iceberg" in a revolution that is presently reshaping the railroad industry from the ground up.

We have seen how strategic mergers are streamlin-ing the nationwide rail network, how modern travel habits have altered the public need for intercity passenger service, how the railroads have capitalized on imaginative new concepts in equipment and service for freight customers, and how modern technology has vastly increased the efficiency of railroad operations.

All of these and little-known — but highly significant — changes have been under way for the last ten to twenty-five years. And they are still in progress as the railroad industry advances quietly from yesterday to tomorrow with the electric Metroliners and gas-turbine powered Turbo trains as the show pieces of the interim period.[10]

Turbo train being serviced in the Toronto yard of the Canadian National Railways. (Photo by author.)

GLOSSARY

A.A.R. The Association of American Railroads.

Headquartered in Washington, the A.A.R. represents the common interests of the industry in such matters as law, operations, maintenance, research, safety, management systems, finance, accounting, economics, public relations, and advertising.

The A.A.R. active membership consists of 116 line-haul railroads, twenty-two switching and terminal companies, and one leased line, all in the United States. In addition, five Canadian Railroads and five Mexican railroads belong to the A.A.R.

The A.A.R. was organized in 1934 by the consolidation of the American Railway Association, the Association of Railway Executives, the Railway Accounting Officers Association, the Railway Treasury Officers Association, and the Bureau of Railway Economics. Eight other organizations were brought into the A.A.R. by the end of 1934.[11]

AIR BRAKES. Power brakes operated by compressed air to control train speed and to stop trains.

The air brake was invented by George Westinghouse and patented by him in 1869. He developed an improved "plain automatic" brake in 1872.[12]

AIR COMPRESSOR. Supplier of compressed air for brake system and all auxillary air-driven equipment. It is driven off the main crank shaft of the diesel engine or by means of separate electric motors.

ALTERNATOR. An electrical generator that produces alternating current (AC). Alternating current drives the traction motor blower. (Traction motor blowers force fresh air over the traction motors to keep them cool during operation).

Note: On the new -2 series of EMD locomotives, the diesel engine drives a main alternator instead of the main generator in older model diesel-electric locomotives.

A-UNIT. A lead locomotive that has a control cab and can operate independently of others. They are equipped for multiple-unit control that allows the engineer in the lead locomotive to control all other locomotives pulling the train from his own cab. A-units are somtimes accompanied by B-units that are of similar carbody design.

AUXILLARY GENERATOR. A generator that furnishes current for charging batteries and for low-

Locomotive 1785 is an F7A unit. 4156 behind it is an FP7 B-unit. The B-unit has no control cab. (Photo by author.)

voltage circuits on the locomotive and the train. Auxillary generators are driven through flexible couplings or by means of belts or gears.

BALLAST

Ballast is material such as gravel, crushed rock, slag, or cinders, placed on the roadbed to drain water away from the ties, to spread the track load over softer subgrade, and to provide an even bearing for the ties, to hold the ties in place, and to check the growth of grass and weeds.[13]

BORE. The inside diameter of cylinders in a diesel engine, expressed in inches per cylinder.

BOXCAR MARKINGS.

In addition to the boxcar number, railroad trademark, and the name or initials of the boxcar's owner, these abbreviations have been adopted as standard markings and are stenciled on both sides of the car:

   CAPY   capacity in pounds
   LD LMT   load limit, in pounds
   LT WT   light weight, in pounds
   EXW   extreme width
   EW   eaves width
   IL   inside length
   IW   inside width
   IH   inside height
   CU FT   cubic foot capacity
   BLT   date built

The load limit is determined by a formula based on size of the journal bearings less the light weight of the car. Capacity is a nominal round figure somewhat less than the load limit.[14]

B-UNIT. A locomotive without a control cab, used as a power unit that assists in hauling trains with A-units with multiple-unit control (see picture above at A-unit).

CABOOSE

The rear car of the freight train — where the crew rides and where supplies, signals, and emergency tools are kept — was variously known in the early days as "Cabin car," "conductor's van," "Brakeman's cab," "accommodation car," "train car," and "way car."

The term *caboose* was used as early as 1855 in reference to the cabin cars on the Buffalo, Corning, and New York Railroad (now part of the Erie-Lackawanna). So far as is known, early cabooses were not equipped with cupolas. This distinctive rooftop feature of the modern caboose is said to have originated in 1863 with T. B. Watson, a freight conductor of the Chicago and Northwestern Railway, in Iowa.

Modern cabooses are equipped with bunks, heaters, lockers, a refrigerator, a desk, toilet facilities, and radio communications equipment. On some cabooses, the cupola has been replaced by a bay window, which provides trainmen with a side view of the train instead of an overhead view.[15]

CARS. The vehicles of the railroad in and on which

Baltimore and Ohio bay-window caboose at the end of truck train. (Photo by author.)

Erie-Lackawanna caboose with cupola. Note sliding screens over windows to protect glass from flying objects. (Photo by author.)

move freight and passengers. Freight cars include such things as boxcars, gondolas, hoppers, covered hoppers, flatcars, tank cars, and cabooses. Passenger cars include coaches, diners, sleepers, baggage cars, and observation cars.

CLASS. A collection of objects grouped together because of common features, functions, traits, or capabilities.

COUPLERS. Mechanical devices that connect two or more railroad cars together and that can be opened to separate them.

DIESEL, DR. RUDOLPH. (1858–1913) German inventor of the internal combustion engine that burns fuel

oil. His creation bears his name — the diesel engine.

DIESEL-ELECTRIC LOCOMOTIVE. A locomotive that consists of one or more units that contain one or more power plants. Each power plant is made up of a diesel engine (the prime mover), which drives the main generator or, in the newer models, the main alternator, supplying electricity to the traction motors geared to each driving axle. (Opposite is an inside look at the parts of a diesel-electric locomotive).

DIESEL ENGINE.
A type of internal combustion engine that burns fuel oil distilled from crude oil: the ignition is brought

Penn Central No. 4898 (ex-Pennsylvania Railroad) GG1 electric locomotive in New Haven, Connecticut. (Courtesy of John B. Egan.)

about by heat resulting from air compression instead of by an electric spark like a gasoline engine.[16]

DYNAMIC BRAKES.

Some locomotives are provided with additional electrical equipment permitting a portion of the power developed by the momentum of the train to be converted into an effective negative power, retarding the speed of the train. This feature is known as *the dynamic brake* and is especially useful as a holding brake, on descending grades.

The traction-motor armatures, being geared to the axles, are rotating whenever the train is moving. When using the dynamic brake, electrical circuits are set up that change the traction motors into generators. Since it takes power to rotate a generator, this action retards the train. The power thus generated is dissipated in resistors, called *grids*, which are cooled by a motor-driven fan. The grids and fan are located in the top of the carbody. The grid-cooling fan receives power that is generated by the "traction motor."[17]

ELECTRIC LOCOMOTIVE. A locomotive using an external source of electricity to run rather than generating its own with a diesel engine. This type of locomotive is used to pull commuter trains in high-speed service and in urban areas where pollution of the air is a problem.

FREIGHT. A load, cargo, or burden carried by a railroad. Also the term given a train that hauls goods rather than passengers.

FREIGHT CAR RECORD KEEPING.

Each railroad has a car record office. By means of conductor's wheel reports (showing cars in each train), interchange reports (showing cars interchanged at junction points), and reports received by teletype from yard offices, each car record office keeps a complete, up-to-date record of the movements of all freight cars on its own lines and all or its own cars on other railroads.

When a car moves from one road to another, it is reported to the car record offices of the railroads concerned, including the railroad that owns the car. Data processing machines speed the work of car record offices.

Increasingly, railroads are turning the technique made possible by the computer and other advanced technology to do a more efficient job of pinpointing equipment location.

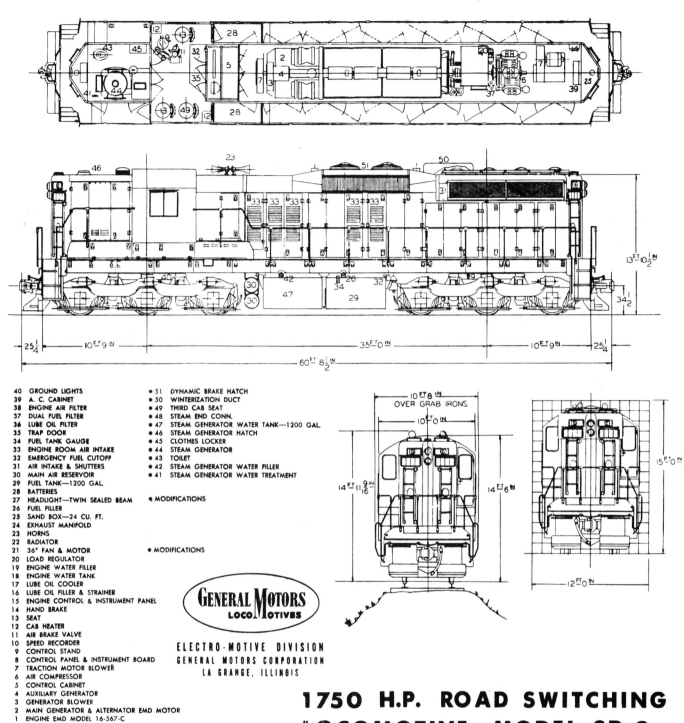

40 GROUND LIGHTS	• 51 DYNAMIC BRAKE HATCH
39 A. C. CABINET	• 50 WINTERIZATION DUCT
38 ENGINE AIR FILTER	• 49 THIRD CAB SEAT
37 DUAL FUEL FILTER	• 48 STEAM END CONN.
36 LUBE OIL FILTER	• 47 STEAM GENERATOR WATER TANK—1200 GAL.
35 TRAP DOOR	• 46 STEAM GENERATOR HATCH
34 FUEL TANK GAUGE	• 45 CLOTHES LOCKER
33 ENGINE ROOM AIR INTAKE	• 44 STEAM GENERATOR
32 EMERGENCY FUEL CUTOFF	• 43 TOILET
31 AIR INTAKE & SHUTTERS	• 42 STEAM GENERATOR WATER FILLER
30 MAIN AIR RESERVOIR	• 41 STEAM GENERATOR WATER TREATMENT
29 FUEL TANK—1200 GAL.	
28 BATTERIES	
27 HEADLIGHT—TWIN SEALED BEAM	• MODIFICATIONS
26 FUEL FILLER	
25 SAND BOX—24 CU. FT.	
24 EXHAUST MANIFOLD	
23 HORNS	
22 RADIATOR	
21 36" FAN & MOTOR	• MODIFICATIONS
20 LOAD REGULATOR	
19 ENGINE WATER FILLER	
18 ENGINE WATER TANK	
17 LUBE OIL COOLER	
16 LUBE OIL FILLER & STRAINER	
15 ENGINE CONTROL & INSTRUMENT PANEL	
14 HAND BRAKE	
13 SEAT	
12 CAB HEATER	
11 AIR BRAKE VALVE	
10 SPEED RECORDER	
9 CONTROL STAND	
8 CONTROL PANEL & INSTRUMENT BOARD	
7 TRACTION MOTOR BLOWER	
6 AIR COMPRESSOR	
5 CONTROL CABINET	
4 AUXILIARY GENERATOR	
3 GENERATOR BLOWER	
2 MAIN GENERATOR & ALTERNATOR EMD MOTOR	
1 ENGINE EMD MODEL 16-567-C	

General Motors LOCOMOTIVES

ELECTRO-MOTIVE DIVISION
GENERAL MOTORS CORPORATION
LA GRANGE, ILLINOIS

1750 H.P. ROAD SWITCHING
LOCOMOTIVE—MODEL SD-9

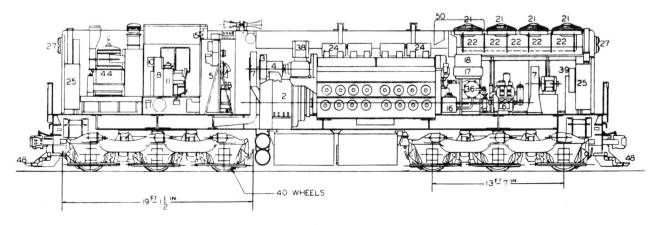

Automatic Car Identification is one of the most important of these new tools. ACI is a system of color-coded labels attached to the sides of freight cars. These labels, which can be read by track-side scanners at speeds of up to eighty miles an hour during all types of weather, contain the car owner's name, car number, and other information.[18]

FREIGHT LOCOMOTIVE. A locomotive designed especially for the carrying and transferring of heavy cargoes by rail. They are built for tremendous pulling power and, if used in road service, for high-speed operation.

FREIGHT TRAIN.
Over a recent ten-year period, the average freight train was composed of about seventy cars and a caboose. This is substantially longer than were trains in previous years. In 1929, the average train was only forty-eight cars long. Some trains have been run experimentally with as many as 500 cars.

Freight cars vary in length from 25 to 125 feet. They average about 45 feet.[19]

GAUGE.
Gauge is the distance between rails of a track, the gauge line being measured at a point ⅝-inch below the top of the rail. The standard gauge — 4′ – 8½″ — was established first in England by George Stephenson, builder of the first successful steam locomotives and the first practical railway. By 1887, every important railroad in this country was using the 4′ – 8½″ gauge.

Among Class I railroads, only the Denver & Rio Grande Western line between Durango and Silverton, Colorado is narrow gauge.[20]
(The gauge is 3′ 0″.)

GENERAL-PURPOSE LOCOMOTIVE. One built to be capable of performing several sorts of work, be it long-haul freight, switching passenger work, or short-distance transfers.

GEAR RATIO. The relationship of the sizes of gears in the drive of the traction motors. A low-gear ratio would be one that delivers great power but low speed, a high-gear ratio is one that delivers less pulling power, but great speed.

GENERATOR, MAIN. An electrical machine with electrical conductors that rotate past electromagnetic poles so that mechanical energy is converted to electrical energy. The main generator is driven by the diesel engine.

GRADE CROSSING. A point of intersection of a railroad embankment and a highway at similar elevation, same height. They are marked with an X with an R to the right and left of the X.

HUMP. The hill or high spot at the head of a hump yard up which cars are pushed, disconnected, and allowed to roll down the opposite side for distribution in the yard.

HUMPING. The action of pushing railroad cars up an embankment, rolling them down the opposite side, and sorting them out for the makeup of trains in a hump yard. Modern hump yards are ultrasophisticated, computer-operated car sorters. They are reputedly one of the major advances in twentieth-century railroading.

JOURNAL BEARINGS. The end of a rotating axle that rests in a bearing, a smooth, oiled surface inside a containing box called a *journal box*.

Open journal box on a boxcar. (Photo by author.)

LOCOMOTIVE.
An engine that can move about by its own power; an electric, steam, or diesel engine on wheels, designed to push or pull a railroad train.[21]

MULTIPLE-UNIT CONTROL. An electrical linkage by which locomotives may be coupled together as a series of locomotives and all operated from the cab of the lead locomotive by one engineer.

MAINLINE. The major route or routes, busiest tracks of a railroad between primary areas of trade or commerce such as large cities. It is generally the most direct route of travel between major geographic areas.

MODIFICATION. An alteration, change, adaptation worked upon a locomotive either by the owner or the manfacturer to suit a specific need of the railroad or to correct some deficiency.

PASSENGER CARS.
About 15,000 passenger-train cars are operated by the U.S. railroads. Of these, about 8,200 are passenger-carrying cars. The remainder include equipment such as U.S. Mail cars, baggage cars, parlor cars, dining cars, and lounge cars. There are a number of variations of these cars.[22]

POWER PLANT. One diesel engine (the prime mover), main generator (or alternator), air compressor, one or more auxillary generators, and the necessary hardware that connects and controls them. There may be more than one power plant in one locomotive, although the vast majority have only one.

RAILROAD.
A railroad is...the right-of-way containing a double bank of steel rails, fixed to the ground on ties, for the use of locomotives and cars to carry goods and people from one point to another. ... A railroad is ... buildings and yards where people work and where rolling stock and motive power are serviced and stored.[23]

RAILS.
The present standard length (of rails) is 39 feet. Some railroads, however, use 45-, 60-, and 78-foot rails in highway-road grade crossings, station platforms, and other special locations.

Rails have usually been joined together in track by means of two pieces of specially shaped, specially treated bars called *joint bars*, or *rail joints*. However, in recent years, through development of improved welding methods, an increasing number of rail joints have been eliminated.

Rails that are welded together at the ends to form a single rail hundreds or thousands of feet in length are known as *continuous rails*. Among the advantages of continuous rails are a smoother track, longer service life, and a reduced maintenance cost.

Rails ranging in weight from 45 to 174 pounds per yard are in use on the Class I railroads of the United States. On truck lines, rail weights range from 85 pounds upward.[24]

RIGHT-OF-WAY.
The right-of-way is the strip of land, of various widths, upon which the railroad and its facilities are built. It is wide enough to provide for tracks, drainage, signals, bridge abutments, telegraph and telephone lines, sidings, buildings and other needs.[25]

ROADBED. The crushed stone, slag, cinders and so forth laid as a base to support the ties and rails of the track.

SHORTLINE. Typically a small, independent railroad working in sparsely active areas between larger rail centers, ferrying cars from larger lines to out-of-the-way customers and back again.

SHUNTING. The action of shifting, switching, and moving cars from one track to another. This is work performed by switching locomotives.

SIDINGS. Spur tracks used to store or spot cars off through tracks. Industries and businesses have sidings on which to keep cars they wish to load and unload with merchandise.

SIGNALS.
Fixed or wayside signals along the track are called *block signals* because they divide the railroad into sections or blocks. They are so spaced that trains will run a safe distance from each other. The basis of today's block system is an electric current flowing through the rails. When all switches are closed — and no train or other obstruction is in the block — the signal shows clear. When a train enters the block, its wheels and axles short-circuit the current, and the signal changes to stop. Usually, the signal circuits are arranged so that a caution signal shows when a train is in the second block ahead.

Block signals give their messages to the engineer through semaphores — signals with movable blades or arms — position-light signals, or color-light signals. Position-light signals have rows of yellow lights instead of semaphore blades. Color light signals — green, yellow, and red — are visible by day as well as by night. Some railroads use a combination of position-and color-light signals.[26]

Cab signals, giving the same indication as the wayside signal, show in miniature on a small panel inside the locomotive cab. Signals are transmitted from the track rails to the engine by electric induction.[27]

SPIKES. Long steel pins, pointed at one end, the other with an oversized head (much like a huge nail) that are used to fasten the rails and tie plates to the wooden crossties. They are driven in with a hammer.

The hook-headed spike, which is used today by railroads to fasten steel rails to crossties, is said to have been designed in 1831 by Robert L. Stevens, the first president of the Camden and Amboy Railroad (now part of the Penn Central) in New Jersey. The first patent for a machine for making hook-headed spikes was issued to Henry Burden of Troy, New York in 1840.[28]

STEAM GENERATOR. A device that furnishes heat for trains by means of an automatically controlled, oil-fired, forced-circulating water-tube generator. A locomotive must have a steam generator to qualify it for freight service.

STROKE. A single, complete movement of a piston in an internal-combustion engine (diesel or gas) from one end of its range to the other. (An engine may be a two-stroke cycle or a four-stroke cycle engine.) A two-stroke or two-cycle engine has a power stroke every revolution of the crankshaft. A four-cycle engine has a power stroke every other revolution of the crankshaft.

SWITCHER. A small locomotive whose task it is to switch or shunt cars from one track to another in a yard area or from through tracks to industrial sidings.

SWITCHES. *See* TURNOUTS.

TIES. The creosote-(wood preservative) treated, hardwood cross members to which are spiked the rails of the tracks.

TIE PLATES.
The plates of steel between the rails and the ties are called *tie plates*. They provide the rail with a uniformly firm foundation, help hold the track gauge, and prevent the rail from cutting into the ties under the heavy impact of trains.[29]

TRACK STRUCTURE.
The track structure consists of ballast, crossties, tie plates, connections, and fastenings. It provides a unique surface of raised rails that, by guiding the flanged wheels of cars, makes it possible to operate trains of cars pulled by locomotives.[30]

TRACTION MOTORS. Variable-speed, direct-current motors geared to the driving axles of a locomotive. They turn the axles to propel the locomo-

A traction motor on a set of locomotive wheels and axle. (Photo by author.)

tive. Traction-motor blowers force air to the traction motors to cool them. In some cases, they may be used as generators (*see* DYNAMIC BRAKES).

TRAIN. A locomotive or locomotives, cars, cargo, and/or passengers traveling coupled together and traveling from one point to another. A line of cars pushed or pulled by a locomotive.

TRUCKS. A framework containing springs, axles, and wheels equipped with a crossmember called a *bolster*, upon which rests the locomotive and/or cars of a railroad. Trucks for both locomotives and cars have two to three axles ordinarily except for very heavy-duty cars and large locomotives that may have four to six.

TURNOUTS. Curved sections of track that branch off other tracks to form still more tracks and sidings. They are also known as *switches*, after the motion of "switching" from one track to another. The curve of turnouts has to be such that locomotives and cars can negotiate them easily. For large locomotives with long trucks, and for high-speed traffic turnouts have to be shallow (slight) curves in order to survive the great impact of heavy traffic. Long wheel-base locomotives will tend to straighten turnouts that are too sharp. This is not good because it destroys the gauge in the track. If the gauge is too wide, trains will not ride the rails, but will take to the ties.

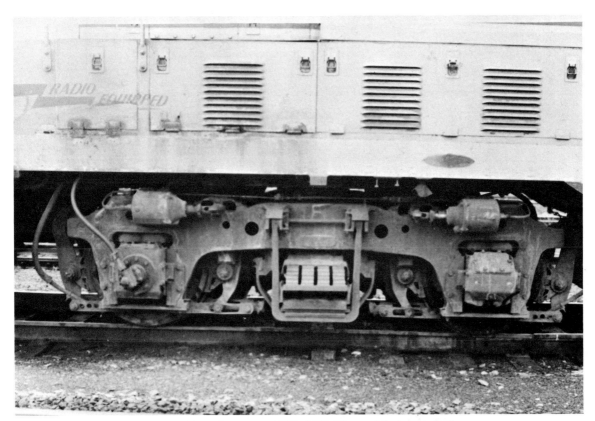

The back truck of an EMD GP7. The cable to the left journal is the speed recorder. The hose to the extreme left of the truck is the sanding line. There is also one at the right side. (Sand is used to prevent wheel slippage.) The small cylinders above the journals are the brake cylinders. In the center of the truck is the big leaf spring, upon which rides the truck bolster. The long sculptured structure facing the viewer is the cast-steel truck sideframe. In this picture, the brakes are engaged and the brake shoes can be seen as the four curved objects in contact with each wheel. The traction motors, not visible here, are mounted one on each of these axles inside the truck. (Photo by author.)

Old hand-operated switch machine at extreme east end of Canadian National yards in Fort Erie, Ontario. (The International Bridge, which spans the Niagara River, is in the background.) The small light on top of the rod on the switch machine turns with the rod (as does the small metal sign) to indicate which way the switch is thrown. (Photo by author.)

UNIT. A single item, one thing. A term used to refer to one locomotive.

UNIT TRAIN.

Unit trains are freight trains moving large tonnages of single bulk products between two points. Unloaded on arrival and returned promptly for another load, such trains cut costs by eliminating intermediate yarding and switching. Begun for coal traffic, unit trains of 100 or more cars also haul grains, ore, and other bulk commodities at sharply reduced rates.[31]

YARDS.

The term *yard* is generally applied to a freight or classification yard, also called a *hump yard*, where switching is done and trains begin and end their runs.

A freight yard is made up of groups or sets of tracks, connected by switches. There are incoming tracks, outbound tracks, and classification tracks where cars are sorted and made up into trains.

Switch engines push trains of incoming cars to the top of an elevation, or hump, where they are cut off, according to their destinations. They are allowed to roll down the sloping hump track into the proper classification tracks, where new trains are being assembled. The switches that turn the cars onto the right tracks are controlled from a tower near the hump.

Towermen also control the speed of the cars by means of electrically or pneumatically operated *car retarders* in the track. These retarders squeeze the sides of moving car wheels with sufficient pressure to slow down or stop them when desired.

A freight yard also has storage tracks, *rip tracks* where cars are given light *running repairs*, and other tracks where freight is loaded and unloaded.

Other types of yards include service yards for cleaning and servicing passenger train cars and locomotive and car-repair yards for outdoor repair work. There are also supporting yards, usually located near an industrial area, where cars assigned to a single plant can be held for quick placement.[32]

NOTES

1. *Railroads of America* (Washington, D.C.: Association of American Railroads, 1970), p. 3.
2. Ibid., pp. 1 – 21.
3. *Webster's New World Dictionary: College Edition.* (Cleveland: World, 1966), p. 861.
4. Railroads of America, pp. 1 – 21.
5. Ibid.
6. Ibid.
7. Ibid.
8. Ibid.
9. Ibid.
10. Ibid.
11. Railroad Quiz (Washington, D.C.: Association of American Railroads, 1970), p. 10.
12. Ibid., p. 6.
13. Ibid.,p. 12.
14. Ibid., p. 20.
15. Ibid., p. 7.
16. Webster's, p.408.
17. Electro-Motive Division Operating Manual for E9 Locomotives (La Grange, Illinois: General Electric, 1954), p. 224.
18. Railroad Quiz, p. 22.
19. Ibid., p. 20.
20. Ibid., p. 12.
21. Webster's, p. 861.
22. Railroad Quiz, p. 25.
23. Railroad Quiz, p. 1.
24. Ibid., pp. 12, 13.
25. Ibid., p. 11.
26. Ibid., pp. 14, 15.
27. Ibid., p. 15.
28. Ibid., p. 12.
29. Ibid., p. 13.
30. Ibid., p. 11.
31. Ibid., p. 23.
32. Ibid., p. 21.

BIBLIOGRAPHY

Car and Locomotive Cyclopedia: 1966 Edition. New York: Combes, C. L., ed. Simmons-Boardman Publishing Corporation, 1966. *See* in particular pp. 962 — 1020.

Pinkepank, Jerry A. *Diesel Spotter's Guide*. Milwaukee, Wisconsin: Kalmbach Publishing Company, 1967. *See* in particular ALCO chapter, pp. ALCO–12 — ALCO–53.

Railroads of America. Washington, D.C.: Association of American Railroads, 1970.

Railroad Quiz. Washington, D.C.: Association of American Railroads, 1970.

Reck, Franklin M., *The Dilworth Story*. New York: McGraw-Hill Book Co. Inc., 1954.

INDEX TO LOCOMOTIVES

INDEX

385.36
R

Roberts, Arthur J.

The American diesel
locomotive

DATE			

4/79